A Legacy of Fame

Shipping and Shipbuilding on the Clyde

Colin M. Castle

The men hae gane, but left ahint a legacy o' fame,
For honest wark and bonny boats that gied the Clyde its name.
From *The Yairds*, by John F.Fergus

Murdoch Carberry
━━ Publishing ━━

D0416574

Published by   Murdoch Carberry Publishing
                97 Park Winding, Erskine PA8 7AT
Printed by   Orr Pollock & Company Limited
                2 Crawfurd Street, Greenock PA15 1LH
Binding: Tweedie & Paterson (Bookbinders)
                4 Back Causeway, Parkhead, Glasgow

First Published March 1990
Copyright © Colin M. Castle
ISBN 0 951 3574 1 7

For Jill and Kerr

Front Cover
Glasgow Harbour, late 1920s from a painting by James Currie Burnie
(1911-1989). Reproduced by permission of Alistair Kerr, Kerprints.

Contents

Acknowledgements

The author wishes to thank the following individuals and organisations for their valuable assistance in the production of this book:
Staff at the Glasgow Museum of Transport, the Glasgow Room of the Mitchell Library and the Scottish Maritime Museum;
Michael Moss, Senior Archivist of the Glasgow University Archives;
Keith Robinson, Director of the Scottish Centre for Social Subjects;
Miss Pat Malcolm, Reference Librarian, Clydebank District Library;
Editorial Staff of the publications *Sea Breezes* and *Ships Monthly*.
To Graham Langmuir I express my gratitude for taking the time to read and comment helpfully on the manuscript.
Special thanks to Alan McKay and to James Smith for their admirable artwork.
Finally, a big thank you to Margaret Stewart for her unstinting clerical assistance.

Illustrations

For their help in obtaining photographic material and granting permission for use, the author and publisher thank:

Glasgow Museums and Art Galleries (pages 22, 30); Alistair Kerr, Kerprints (page 48); Brian Walsh (page 52); Wotherspoon Collection, Mitchell Library (pages 62, 79); Thomas Annan & Company (page 63); Laurence Dunn Collection (pages 80, 97, 98, 104); SKYFOTOS (page 103), F Leonard Jackson (page 108), Clydebank District Libraries (page 110).

Foreword

Arguably, the Clyde is the most prolific shipbuilding river in the world, with more than 35,000 ships built in its history. This publication encapsulates the facts, the entrepreneurial ability and the craftsmanship of the people who owned and built the ships. It can be seen from the book that many of the shipyards were owned by the shipping companies and this formed a strong bond for the growth of the industry. Unfortunately we are often the victims of progress and this great industry is but a shadow of its former self. However, one or two yards look like surviving and thus continue the tradition that 'Clyde-built' ships are still the best.

I have certainly enjoyed reading it and I am sure it will give many a Clydesider a lump in his throat when he reads about the ships he built, because like all shipbuilders every ship we build carries a bit of us with it.

Eric Mackie
Former Managing Director, Kvaerner Govan Limited.

Author's Preface

When Better By Yards was published in the summer of 1988 I little anticipated the enthusiastic response it would generate. Local readers, former shipyard workers, historians and shipping buffs from countries as diverse as Canada, Denmark, France and Poland enjoyed the book and its style of presentation. To those who took the time and trouble to write with offers of support, advice and constructive criticism I tender my sincere thanks.

This new book follows the format of its predecessor, having chapters devoted to histories of major Clydeside shipyards and Clyde-based shipping lines. Case studies of a further thirty famous vessels built on the Clyde are also included, while an appendix detailing the principal nineteenth century Clyde yards brings to a conclusion the catalogue of shipbuilding enterprises on the river over the past 190 years.

Colin M. Castle

The Shipping Market

More than 30,000 ships have been launched from the banks of the Clyde in the last 150 years. The Industrial Revolution of the late-eighteenth and nineteenth centuries witnessed the development of the steam engine providing the motive power for successive genera-tions of factory machinery and equipment. Its application as a means of marine propulsion was quickly recognised and exploited by early shipbuilding pioneers like the Napiers, Dennys, David Elder, David Tod and John MacGregor so that by the beginning of the twentieth century the Clyde shipyards had developed and refined their con-struction and manufacturing techniques to the acme of perfection. Sail was largely discarded in favour of the reciprocating engine and the steam turbine shortly thereafter. Within the space of 80 years Henry Bell's humble *Comet*, which had first ventured out on the Firth in 1812 heralding in the age of steam propulsion, had been superseded by the ocean giant of 10,000 tons or more and the Clyde's international reputation as 'shipbuilder to the world' firmly established.

It is tempting to regard shipbuilding's 'Golden Age' from a some-what lyrical standpoint but the reality was rather different. This was an industry of fluctuating fortunes with many yards stumbling from one financial crisis to another. Some collapsed completely while others experiencing economic hardship were acquired cheaply by direct take-over or corporate merger. Forecasting demand was made doubly difficult for the yards as they had to rely on the market projections of the shipping companies, who did not always get it right. The years after the Second World War saw the fortunes of the shipbuilders on Clydeside lapse into decline. This was attributable to a number of diverse and often unrelated factors which included the rapid drop in the nation's emigration figures (at one time the bread-and-butter of shipowners); the growth of state-subsidised foreign competition; the pressures exerted on the industry by the emergence of cheap and reliable air travel at the expense of the liner market which had no long-term prospect of recovery and an excess yard capacity for actual or projected demands. These factors were clearly identifiable by the late fifties but the process of decline had been a slow and inexorable one whose source dated back to a much earlier period and was inextricably bound up with the economics of shipbuilding as a whole.

1

When it came to tendering for a contract many yards pared back costs to the bone. Given the financial variables which came into play in the construction of a ship, such a policy was akin to playing Russian Roulette. In the 1840's most yards could tender for any contract and almost guarantee success, but by the 1880's things had changed and companies were being forced into cut-throat competition to gain orders, some of which were recognised as loss-makers from the start. It is not difficult to understand why such policies were adopted. As early as 1834 Robert Napier had built the *Dundee* and the *Perth* for the Dundee, Perth and London Shipping Company at a price far below the vessels' construction costs thereby incurring losses. Napier explained his actions in a letter to a close friend:

In getting up the first of these vessels great care and attention would be necessary to gain the different objects in view and in doing this an extra expense may be incurred, but which may be avoided in all other vessels.

Offering a financial carrot of this nature in the hope of attracting further contracts was sensible if a yard was building a number of vessels over a twelve month period, but it spelt disaster when applied to a large, complex single order which might occupy the greater part of a yard's production capacity. Even if the firm emerged in profit at the end of such work the rewards were often minimal as the table below illustrates:

SHIP	DATE	COST	PROFIT	LOSS
City of New York	1888 ⎫	£900,000		£10,250
City of Paris	1888 ⎭			
Campania	1893 ⎫	£1.3m		£80,000
Lucania	1893 ⎭			
Saxonia	1899	£400,000		£9,478
Lusitania	1906	£1.6m	£50,972*	
Aquitania	1913	£1.4m	£19,489	

* The profit margin was greater for this vessel because costs were partially offset by Government subsidy

By contrast naval orders yielded greater profits, which led some yards to become preoccupied with work of this nature. Warships took twice as long to build as passenger ships of the same tonnage and occupied for longer periods berths normally reserved for liner tonnage. Even so the profit margins were attractive and tempted yards

2

like Fairfield, Brown and Beardmore to invest in plant and equipment for the naval market before, during and after the First World War. In the case of J & G Thomson (later John Brown and Company) the decision to purchase its Clydebank site was heavily influenced by the profitability of these contracts and prompted William Beardmore to construct his magnificent yard at Dalmuir so as to be able to take on greater, more ambitious naval projects. In John Brown's case the move appeared to pay off initially. For the period 1899 to 1913 yard sales totalled £11.8M; £6.5M of this came from naval orders and £5.3M from merchant work. Total gross profit on this figure was £3.3M returning £782,000 net profit after allowances for depreciation and overheads. Naval work represented 55% of total sales but yielded 68% of gross and 88% of net profit. These margins were substantial; eg. the battleship *HMS Leviathan* cost £705,000 to build but afforded a net profit of £144,937, while the dreadnought battle-cruiser *HMS Inflexible* cost £1,249,782 with a net profit of £124,809 accruing.

Not all yards hastened to invest in this naval market however. The Board of Directors at the Belfast firm of Harland and Wolff viewed Clydeside's preoccupation with defence contracts as a heaven-sent opportunity to 'poach' from it valued customers who previously had long-standing relationships with Clyde yards. By choosing not to build naval vessels the management established the Belfast yard as one of the premier mercantile shipbuilding organisations in the United Kingdom.

In the post-war world of 1919-1920 shipyard expansion continued on the Clyde. Fairfield's Board authorised the spending of £70,000 on the development of its West Yard and a further £30,000 on their engineering and boiler works. £27,445 was expended on the formation of Berth Number 6 to the east of the yard. Further down river at Linthouse, Stephen's extended their engine works to such an extent that they were capable of producing output in excess of the yard's capacity to produce hulls. By December 1919 the shipyard found itself short of capital and unable to finance expansion plans estimated to cost £100,000. Beardmore too built four new berths at Dalmuir in anticipation of further Admiralty contracts.

This frenzied activity coupled with a wartime excess profit tax severely weakened the liquidity of many notable Clyde shipbuilders, and this in time led to structural changes in the industry, either through amalgamations or cartel agreements with shipowning companies to ensure survival. Some of these proved to be of an unstable or dubious nature and inevitably came to an ignominious end.

In 1919 the Royal Mail Shipping Group headed by Sir Owen Philipps (later Lord Kylsant) acquired Harland and Wolff gaining in the process the London and Glasgow Shipbuilding and Engineering Company Limited, which the Belfast company had bought over in 1912, and the Greenock-based yard of Caird and Company (taken over in 1916). RMS then acquired A & J Inglis of Pointhouse and the Meadowside yard of D & W Henderson. In addition to its shipbuilding acquisitions the Royal Mail Group controlled numerous shipping lines. By 1929 it had taken over no less than 26 companies including the Pacific Steam Navigation Company, Lamport and Holt, Elder Dempster, Bullard King and Company, the Coast, Shire, Glen, Nelson, Union-Castle and White Star Lines. Clarence Hatry's Northumberland Shipbuilding Company secured majority share-holdings in Fairfield and the Blythswood Shipbuilding Company in 1920, while Lord Inchcape, chairman of the P & O Group, became principal shareholder in Alexander Stephen & Sons. The personalities responsible for these mergers and acquisitions all predicted boom conditions in the aftermath of the Great War and saw that by buying into shipbuilding firms they could secure a ready supply of new tonnage at low prices in what was believed to be a highly competitive market. Such a notion was disastrous; the post-war boom failed to materialise and depression set in. Empty order books forced ship-builders and owners alike to bolster up their tottering consortia by using up their liquid capital, and some, like Philipps and Hatry, faced bankruptcy and ended up in prison for fraudulent practices. Philipps' incarceration signalled the demise of the Royal Mail Shipping Group which collapsed under the cumulative burden of its collective debt resulting in ultimate losses to shareholders of £50 million, a stagger-ing sum for that time.

If the fortunes of the mercantile market appeared to be foundering there was little comfort for those who sought salvation in attracting naval contracts. As a nation the British had done with war, and public reaction to the rearmament programme was at best lukewarm during the twenties. International affairs also had a part to play. In Decem-ber 1921 the Washington Naval Treaty, a four-power agreement to which Great Britain was a signatory, was concluded. For some time the USA had been expressing concern over Japanese expansion in the Pacific and was determined to halt it. Surprisingly the Japanese agreed and promptly cancelled orders for three battleships each to have been built in British yards. These vessels would have been more powerful than anything the Americans or British had to offer, but as

4

the signatories were eager to avoid an arms race similar to that which preceded the Great War, an amicable settlement was reached. This had a devastating effect on British shipyards and their ancillary industries and, in the case of the Beardmore Company for whom one of the ships had been earmarked, dealt it a blow from which it never recovered. For much of the twenties and thirties the shipbuilding industry faced severe recession and, with its virtual collapse on Clydeside in the early thirties, most firms closed down until the economy took an upturn in the last few years before the Second World War.

The Post-War Years

When World War Two came to an end the future for the British shipbuilding industry looked bright, particularly for Clydeside, since this area had traditionally been in the forefront of the national shipbuilding programme. The rearmament plans of the late thirties had succeeded in dragging the industry out of the years of depression, and the defeat of Germany and Japan, accompanied by the devastation wrought on their industrial sectors, seemed to have removed almost all the barriers confronting the British yards. Britain was therefore in a most favourable position to replace the shipping losses of the war years and provide for the world-wide demand for new tonnage.

For some ten years the industry did experience a 'boom' period, with the demand for shipping exceeding supply. However, shipbuilding by its very nature seemed prone to a series of booms and recessions. Most ships had a life expectancy of 10 to 20 years and so renewal was estimated at between 3% and 4% per annum. Even the slightest increase could lead to feverish activity in the industry while a reduction in demand would have the opposite effect. By the mid-fifties Britain was no longer the market leader. The factors leading to this state of affairs were not difficult to identify.

Because of the length of time between placing an order for a vessel and its final delivery, both cost and delivery time were quoted when tenders were submitted for a contract. The time lapse could be as much as three years in some cases and costs could be adversely affected by the effects of inflation on for example a yard's wage bill or the prices of component parts. For the shipbuilder the final cost of delivery might well be greater than the original tender. In the mid-fifties inflation in the UK was running at a higher rate than that of her shipbuilding competitors, and Japan especially was willing to take on contracts at a fixed price, making her yards more competitive than their British counterparts. In order to compete with these foreign shipyards many British firms pared tenders back to the margin which in many cases led to the incurring of large financial losses because of inflation, labour disputes or time penalty clauses.

Although the amount of shipping launched in the UK continued to rise during the 50's, Britain's share of the world market was falling dramatically. The picture would have been much gloomier if there had not still existed the demand for replacement tonnage worldwide. However the shipyards of some other nations were in a better position to satisfy the needs of the mercantile sector than those in the UK. Japan had not suffered any damage to her shipyards, but as part of her post-war economic recovery drive (which was financed by the USA) her yards were modernised and their capacity extended. German yards too were completely rebuilt using allied funds while those in Sweden had also come through the war unscathed. In all these countries new mass production techniques and standardisation were introduced by efficient management.

By the mid-fifties unit replacement for shipping fleets fell off rapidly. British yards had made a start on heavy capital investment but poor labour relations negated many of the possible benefits. Traditionally, great numbers of workers were made redundant whenever a ship was launched from a British yard, and it was because of this that some shipyard unions, the boilermakers in particular, had turned towards restrictive practices in an attempt to maintain levels of employment. In this atmosphere many disputes and strikes emerged and demarcation disputes were rife:

The delays resulting from demarcation practices may be illustrated from the fitting of a port light. This requires a shipwright to mark the position for the light, a driller to prepare a centre guide hole, a caulker to make the opening, a driller to drill the side holes and a caulker to bolt the light and attach the chain; each tradesman being summoned by his foreman and the operations carried out in sequence.

The effect of bad industrial relations can be seen in the table overleaf. Disputes frequently placed contract work behind schedule with the imposition of penalty clauses for late delivery. This in turn discouraged ship owners from placing repeat orders with the shipyards in question.

6

Tonnage Launched per Shipyard Worker per Year		
YEAR	UK	SWEDEN
1954	18.8	20.5
1955	19.3	24.2
1956	17.4	20.9
1957	18.5	25.6
1958	18.4	31.0

The situation was further aggravated by the rapid decline in the specialised passenger shipbuilding market due to the growth of passenger air services. In time this would be clearly demonstrated by the fates of the great Cunarders, especially the two *Queens*. In this market, yards like Fairfield, John Brown and Belfast's Harland and Wolff reigned supreme. The Clyde builders were struck a bodyblow from which they would never recover.

Faced with this situation the British government authorised the Geddes Report of 1966 to investigate and give recommendations which would lead to the strengthening of British shipbuilding against ever increasing foreign competition. The solution as they saw it was the fusion of certain yards on the Clyde's upper reaches which came to be known as Upper Clyde Shipbuilders.

On the Lower Clyde, Lithgow at Port Glasgow, Scott's Shipbuilding and Engineering Company Ltd and, at Scotstoun, Yarrow and Company were able to remain independent for much of the post-war era. Lithgow's Kingston yard was reconstructed to build very large crude oil carriers. When demand began to fall, the Lithgow Group consolidated its position by closing down two of their three engine works, Rankin and Blackmore and David Rowan and Company, leaving John Kincaid and Company as their only engine builders. Scotts had always effectively straddled the naval, passenger and cargo ship markets by building submarines, second and third rate liners, oil tankers and general cargo vessels, and possessed the prime shipbuilding site on the Firth. Regardless, in the wake of the Geddes Report both Scott and Lithgow were forced to amalgamate. Upper Clyde Shipbuilders came into existence in February 1968 but from its inception it encountered a great number of financial problems.

The first of these occurred when the newly created Shipbuilding Industry Board, under some government pressure, granted a loan of £5.5m to the consortium. Of this £3.5m was to be handed over at once with the remaining £2m held in reserve. In the event only £1.2m of this latter figure was ever drawn, for the purpose of providing a covered yard at Yarrow and Company Ltd, but less than a year later UCS was requesting a further £3.5m in the form of equity plus £5.5m in outright grants to see it through its teething troubles and, once again, the SIB obliged. Three months later the consortium was in deep financial trouble for a third time but was rescued by the intervention of the then Minister of Technology, Anthony Wedgewood Benn, who secured a loan of £7m on easy interest terms, but not through the SIB. Shortly after this an arrangement was reached whereby UCS's acquired interest in Yarrows (initially a consortium member) was to be returned to that company allowing it to function as an independent concern.

The change of government in 1970 brought a change in economic philosophy and, when yet again UCS reported financial difficulties, it was announced that the financial guarantees to UCS from the SIB would be withdrawn. The Conservative Government argued that it was not their duty to maintain these guarantees as they had only been made to shipbuilders to allow them credits and capital to complete their existing orders. John Davies, the Secretary of State for Trade and Industry, spoke of the situation at UCS during the Conservative Party Conference and his 'lame-duck' philosophy soon became clear. There was no room in the competitive world for inefficient, uneconomic industrial or commercial enterprises. The accounts staff at UCS worked non-stop to prepare financial statements which would be acceptable to the government and lead to the restoration of credits. This outcome was on the point of being reached when, at the eleventh hour, Yarrows refused to honour the agreement concerning its break with UCS. Chairman Eric Yarrow wanted, as the price for withdrawing from the consortium and going independent, a proportional share of the loans and grants given to UCS over the years. This provoked much hostility among the workers on Clydeside since Yarrows were to receive, as a free gift, the covered berth built by UCS at a cost of £1.2m. Despite this the government agreed to restore the SIB's credit guarantees but less than three months later UCS informed them that there was no money to pay their outstanding wage bills. The chairman of the group, Anthony Hepper, went to London and informed the SIB, which represented the government, that unless a further £10m was forthcoming, UCS Limited would have to place its affairs in the hands of a liquidator. As an interim measure John Davies agreed to pay the wage bill for the coming week (13th June 1971) but because the unions in UCS would not tolerate a 20% cut in wages nor would the company's creditors agree to freeze its debts, the decision facing the government was twofold: either inject massive amounts of financial capital into the enterprise or allow it to collapse. On 14th June it was announced that UCS would go into liquidation, but Davies added that a group of individuals from both the government and shipbuilding industry sides would look into all aspects of the crisis with a view to recommending some form of reconstruction of the yards on the Upper Clyde. With the appointment of the provisional liquidator the affairs of UCS Ltd were terminated. The Scottish unemployment figure at that time was 117,000 with male unemployment standing at 7.4% as opposed to England's 4.5%. In Glasgow alone 27,000 were jobless (9.6%). The government's closure of UCS would add a further 8,000 to that figure: 2,500 at Govan, 1,000 at Scotstoun, 2,600 at Clydebank and 400 at Linthouse with a further 290 apprentices and 1,500 general staff. When ancillary industries were taken into account the figure was estimated at between fifteen and twenty thousand. Faced with this prospect, those threatened with redundancy began their famous work-in and succeeded in keeping the plight of the Upper Clyde yards in the public eye. Eventually, after prolonged negotiations, a new shipbuilding company rose from the ashes of the ill-fated UCS grouping.

Govan Shipbuilders was formed in 1972 and administered under government supervision. The old Fairfield yard served as the core of this new entity and incorporated the works of both Stephen and Connell. The latter was managed under a separate company called Scotstoun Marine Limited but supervised directly by the parent company. Until 1988 Govan Shipbuilders was highly successful and succeeded in producing some superbly designed and at times innovative vessels as well as boosting productivity levels. Its main claim to fame lay in the design of standard ships which incorporated a degree of flexibility and so enabled the yard to meet an owner's specialised requirements. During its lifetime more than 60 of these were built, for instance the 'Clyde', 'Kuwait' and 'Cardiff' designs. The yard was also responsible for building the world's largest car ferry in 1987 when North Sea Ferries' *Norsea* was launched with a gross tonnage in excess of 40,000.

In the wake of the UCS collapse the Clydebank yard of John Brown and Company faced the prospect of immediate closure. The Texas firm of Marathon Limited made a successful bid for the company in 1972 and the newly created subsidiary - Marathon (UK) Limited - commenced with a programme of jack-up oil rig building. This was only marginally profitable and in 1980 the Americans withdrew from Clydebank leaving the French owned UIE to take over the site. Several cost-cutting exercises followed including the paring down of the workforce and the renting out of some of the yard's facilities to other commercial concerns. At the time of writing UIE Shipbuilding (Scotland) Limited continues to operate from Clydebank.

With the continuing decline in world shipbuilding generally, the Labour Government decided to nationalise the industry in 1977, viewing this as the only way of guaranteeing its future existence. The yards came under the control of a holding company - British Shipbuilders Limited - who, three years later, reorganised them into five trading divisions. These were: (A) Merchant Shipbuilding Division which incorporated Govan Shipbuilders and Ferguson-Ailsa Limited (B) Warship Building Division incorporating Yarrow Shipbuilders Limited (C) Engineering Division (D) Ship-Repair Division and (E) Offshore Division incorporating Scott Lithgow Limited.

In 1979 the newly elected Conservative Government chose to sell off the profitable sectors of the industry and reduce the enormous losses being made by the others. Scott Lithgow was acquired by the Trafalgar House Group in 1984 while the GEC company took over Yarrow the following year. In 1986 Ferguson-Ailsa was rationalised into one yard at Port Glasgow and amalgamated with the North Devon yard, Appledore Shipbuilders Limited.

During 1988 the fortunes of Govan Shipbuilders suffered a decline. Faced with strong overseas competition the yard repeatedly lost out when tendering for contracts. This was particularly galling when the successful bidder was a French rival whose government heavily subsidised its shipbuilding industry.

With the loss of a substantial order for three vessels for Brittany Ferries Ltd, the Board of Management was faced with an increasingly bleak prospect. Rescue came from an unexpected quarter in the form of the Norwegian firm, Kvaerner Limited, which assumed control of the yard. Known as Kvaerner-Govan Shipbuilders, output is mainly confined to bulk and liquified gas carriers. It is too early to determine the success or failure of this new venture but it is to be hoped that it will prosper for, if the worst were to occur, it would effectively see the end of commercial shipbuilding on the Upper Clyde.

Glasgow Based Shipping Lines

The Albion Line

The Albion Line was a Glasgow-based shipping company owned and operated by the Patrick Henderson Line. By the 1850's the firm was already well-established having a fleet of sailing vessels plying the routes from the Clyde to New Zealand. Most of these ships were two-deckers with emigrant accommodation installed on the lower deck as it was from this source that the Albion Line principally derived its income. The fleet therefore differed in appearance from the standard sailing tramps which had only a single deck and were ideal for carrying general cargoes but totally unsuited for conveying passengers.

Albion however, did not enjoy a monopoly of New Zealand traffic. Shaw, Savill and Company operated a similar service from 1858. By 1866 some sixty-eight of their ships were servicing the major New Zealand ports, while Albion employed the eight that they owned together with a number of others on charter. Even so, the service offered was erratic and attracted much adverse comment especially from New Zealand. Finally, after a further seven years of unreliability and inefficiency the New Zealand government granted permission for the founding of a national shipping company financed by New Zealand capital. It came into existence in January 1873 and traded under the name of the New Zealand Shipping Company Limited. During its first year the company organised 37 sailings to the United Kingdom and maintained exceptionally high standards of performance and reliability much to the cost of both Shaw, Savill and Company and the Albion Line. Meanwhile the growth of the New Zealand trade continued unabated.

In 1875 140 ships left UK ports bound for New Zealand. Half were Shaw, Savill vessels, one third were ships of the New Zealand Shipping Company while the Albion fleet accounted for the remainder. This state of affairs generated healthy competition as it soon became clear that the company which boasted the fastest vessels attracted the greatest volume of traffic and, as a consequence, the prestige. In time the sailing passage norm became one hundred days but much of the glory fell to the New Zealand Shipping Company and not to its British rivals. The need for Shaw, Savill and the Albion Line to present a united front to combat the New Zealand company's ever-increasing share of the market was daily becoming more obvious.

Discussions between the two company boards commenced in 1878 with a view to closer collaboration. The talks came to fruition towards the end of 1882 with the surprising decision to wind up the operations of both firms while at the same time establishing a new organisation to be known as Shaw, Savill and Albion Company Limited. The new entity began trading on 1st January 1883 and produced a fleet of thirty-one sailing ships to handle the New Zealand trade. Of these, twelve were Albion vessels: *Auckland, Canterbury, Dunedin, Invercargill, Jessie Readman, Lyttleton, Nelson, Omaru, Timaru, Wellington, Westland* and *Wild Deer*. These were sold as one lot to the new company for £200,157 cash. Patrick Henderson and Company were appointed Shaw, Savill and Albion's Glasgow agents while the new company's Board of Directors included Peter Denny, the Chairman of Patrick Henderson, and James Galbraith, the manager of the Albion Line.

Although never a major shipping line Albion did boast some fine units within its fleet. The company's first acquisition was the wooden sailing ship *Lady Douglas* in 1856. This small vessel of 594 gross tons was a product of John Scott and Son's yard in Greenock and was built for the Albion Line who subsequently sold her after some sixteen years service. The *City of Dunedin* (1863) was the company's first ship to exceed 1000 gross tons and, like her predecessors, was of wooden construction. She was Albion's largest and finest vessel to date and, despite her name, was intended for the company's Indian service. Her builders were Rankin and Son of Dumbarton and her service with Albion, like the *Lady Douglas*, lasted sixteen years.

Of the twelve Albion ships which formed part of the Shaw, Savill and Albion fleet, six belonged to the splendid 'Auckland' class built by Robert Duncan of Port Glasgow. The *Auckland* itself, which entered service in 1874, was a vessel of 1,308 gross tons. She quickly became known as 'the yacht of the fleet' because of her elegant lines and featured an extended poop which housed the passengers in permanent accommodation. All members of the class were iron-hulled with two decks and capable of making fast passages which made them very popular with the emigrant trade. Throughout the company's life it only ever owned one steamship, the *Taiaroa*. She plied between various New Zealand ports on feeder services during 1875. For reasons which remain unclear, she was disposed of that same year.

Today Shaw, Savill and Albion own no ships and its activities are almost entirely confined to ship management as part of the Furness Withy Consortium. Throughout its history this great line was always in the forefront of shipping design and route leadership and set high standards in both conveyancing of cargo and passenger travel for almost a century. Shaw Savill and Albion's reputation could only be described as impeccable.

The Bank Line (Andrew Weir and Company)

Andrew Weir was born in 1865 in the town of Kirkcaldy. As a young man he worked briefly in a Glasgow shipowner's office before establishing his own business in 1885 with the acquisition of his first ship *Willowbank*, a vessel of 882 gross tons. Within ten years this forceful and dynamic personality was the owner of the largest fleet of sailing ships trading under the British flag.

Olivebank

Andrew Weir and Company's headquarters were initially in Glasgow but moved to London in 1905 as the company rapidly expanded. That same year saw the formation of the Bank Line Limited with branches opened in Middlesbrough, New York, Hong Kong, Buenos Aires and San Francisco. Though the hub of this company's operations had been removed to London, the registered office of the Bank Line remained in Glasgow. At its peak the sailing fleet numbered 45 ships and others were managed during the Great War. The best known Bank vessel of this period was the *Olivebank*, a beautiful steel barque of 2,824 gross tons built by Mackie and Thomson of Glasgow in 1892. She served the company for over twenty years before being sold out of the fleet and then continued to sail the world's oceans until she was mined off Gotland while on passage from Barry to Mariehamn on 8th September 1939. By that time Andrew Weir and Company were principally concerned with insurance in both underwriting and ship brokerage capacities having branches and subsidiaries in the United States, South America, Australia, South Africa, India, Hong Kong, Japan, Burma, Iraq, Ceylon, Northern and Southern Rhodesia and West Africa.

The first steamship to join the line was the *Duneric* of 1896, built by the Campbeltown Shipbuilding Company and engined by Rankin and Blackmore. She had a gross tonnage of 1,878 and a cargo capacity for 3,050 tons deadweight. The growth of the steamer fleet was as rapid as that of the sailers, rising to a total deadweight tonnage of 312,534 by 1914. There was however, a shift in emphasis away from general tramping in favour of operating on regular routes to distant parts of the world. Between 1896 and 1948 no less than eighty-eight steamships were either built for or acquired by the Bank Line. The smallest unit was the *Alert* (327 gross tons) built in 1855 and purchased by Weir in 1898. At one time this Hull-built vessel had been a passenger steamer but was later shortened by some 35 feet while undergoing conversion to a cargo carrier. Her service with the line lasted only a year before she was sold to a Gravesend buyer. The *Aymeric* (4,367 gross tons) was a well-known Bank ship which joined the fleet in 1905, the first new vessel to come under the ownership of the Bank Line Limited. She was completed by Russell and Company of Port Glasgow and gave unstinted service until 1st June 1918 when she was sunk by a U-boat off Cape Matapan. The next year saw the establishment of the firm's India—Africa Line while a new service from Seattle to Australia was inaugurated in 1907. To cope with the ever-increasing demand for vessels the company not only ordered new tonnage but acquired some steamships second hand. One such purchase was the Cunard cargo steamer *Albania* (1900) built by Swan Hunter Limited with a gross tonnage of 7,682. She had been constructed as the *Consuelo* for the Wilson Line and had served the Cairn Line as the *Cairnrona* before joining the Cunard fleet. Her career with that company was unsuccessful and she was subsequently sold to the Bank Line with whom she served for the next sixteen years as the *Poleric*. She had a large cargo capacity of 9,200 tons deadweight and a speed of 11 knots.

In 1917 Andrew Weir was appointed to the office of Surveyor General of Supply at the War Office as a member of the Army Council. He became a member of the Cabinet and Minister of Munitions in January 1919. For his services in these capacities he was created the first Baron Inverforth of Southgate that same year; thereafter he resigned from the partnership of Andrew Weir and Company and was succeeded by his son A Morton Weir.

The post-war fleet, much of it second hand, was largely built up using standard ships constructed during 1918 and 1919. Among these additions were the *Ioseric* (ex-*War Parrot*/4,240 gross tons), *Luceric* (ex-*War Agate*/6,681 grt), *Elveric* (ex-*War Capitol*/5,685 grt), *Aymeric* (ex-*War Nemesis*/5,196 grt), and *Haleric* (ex-*War Sparrow*/5,238 grt). The twenties saw this trend towards the purchase of second hand tonnage continue although four steamers were ordered from the yard of Workman, Clark Limited for delivery in 1929-30. The *Deebank*, *Trentbank*, *Forthbank* and *Lindenbank* were vessels of 5,060 gross tons fitted with quadruple expansion engines capable of speeds up to 11 knots.

Like so many other shipping companies, the Bank Line did not escape the ravages of the Second World War lightly. Among the victims were *Cedarbank*, torpedoed by enemy aircraft in April 1940, *Elmbank* sunk by a U-boat in September the same year and *Thursobank* the following month also to a U-boat attack. Enemy submarines accounted for the *Thornliebank* (November 1941), *Weirbank* (July 1942), *Trentbank* (November 1942), *Tinhow* (May 1943) and *Larchbank* (September 1943) while the *Birchbank* succumbed to air attack in November 1943.

In the period of reconstruction after 1945 the Bank Line sought to return to normality as quickly as possible by purchasing twelve liberty ships to replace some of the company's wartime losses. These vessels had a deadweight capacity of 10,500 tons with a gross tonnage of 7,300 and all had been built during 1943-44. Each had a service speed of 11 knots and all but one continued in Bank Line service until the late-50s.

The transition from steam to diesel propulsion was smoothly accomplished by the company. As early as 1924 the Board of Directors had demonstrated their faith in what was then a novel power source by ordering eighteen motorships, the first of which was the *Gujarat*, a vessel of 4,320 gross tons and a speed of 10 knots. Her success can be gauged by the fact that she remained in service for over thirty years, logging over 1,750,000 miles on her original engine. By the 1950's the fashion for motorships was well-established with the Bank Line in the forefront. Six vessels of 8,900 tons deadweight were ordered from Harland and Wolff in February 1953 followed by eight more from William Doxford and Sons Limited. The *Foylebank* was one of the Belfast ships and representative of both her class and cargo carriers of the period. With an overall length of 455 feet and a service speed of 14 knots she had two steel decks, orlop deck forward of the machinery space, poop, forecastle, lower bridge, navigating bridge and docking bridge decks. There were four main cargo holds, two forward and two aft, and her cargo handling equipment comprised one 25 ton, fourteen 5 ton and two 3 ton tubular steel derricks with fourteen electric winches.

Any review of the Andrew Weir organisation would be incomplete without mention of the vast tanker fleet which was under their management before 1939. These were both motor and steam vessels. The Bank Line first ventured into tanker owning in 1913 with the steamer *Desabla* and during the 1920's managed the fleet of the British-Mexican Petroleum Company Limited which comprised twelve vessels. The Weir Group also managed the Lago Shipping Company Limited and ordered much of its tonnage. These units, each with a tonnage of 2,372 gross, were essentially shallow draft tankers for use on Lake Maracaibo in Venezuela. In the late 30's Andrew Weir and Company assumed the management of Inver Tankers Limited whose fleet consisted of seven motorships ordered from German shipyards. Each vessel carried around 14,000 tons deadweight and was capable of speeds of up to 13 knots. All seven became war losses, the first being the *Inverliffey* (9,456 gross tons) which was torpedoed and sunk by gunfire on 11th September 1939. The last of the class, the *Inverilen*, met a similar fate on 3rd February 1943.

The company continues to trade as shipowners and managers.

British India Steam Navigation Company Limited

In December 1847 William MacKinnon and Robert MacKenzie, both natives of Campbeltown, entered into partnership for the purpose of general trading on the Indian sub-continent. The Calcutta based firm, known as MacKinnon, MacKenzie and Company, prospered from the outset so that within two years it was chartering ships out of Glasgow and Liverpool to deliver cargoes to Calcutta. These were then transshipped overland where other vessels were waiting to convey them to Australia and China. The success of this venture prompted the partners to establish a new concern in 1856, the Calcutta and Burma Steam Navigation Company, with its headquarters in Glasgow. A successful bid for the mail contract between Rangoon and Calcutta was the raison d'etre behind this move and on 24th September the company was registered with a share capital of £35,000. The operation of such a service required the purchase of vessels and was to be the partners' introduction to ship owning. They offered a disciplined and punctual service which did not have to rely on a haphazard collection of tramp steamers and sailing ships. The acquisition of two vessels, the *Baltic* (1854) and the *Cape of Good Hope* (1856), was followed by the inauguration of the mail run between the two ports.

In 1862 MacKinnon pledged to operate a scheduled steamer service from Calcutta to Karachi calling at all ports in between if the Goverment of Bengal agreed to offer a subsidy to help maintain it. The latter expressed some reluctance to finance the scheme but the Governor of Bombay stepped in to provide the necessary capital and the service was established. This was quickly followed by the award of a twice-monthly mail contract between Bombay and Karachi and an eight times a year contract linking Bombay with Basra at the head of the Persian Gulf. At this point MacKinnon proposed that the company's name be changed to the British India Steam Navigation Company Limited which more accurately reflected the scope and field of the company's operations. The name was formally registered on 28th October 1862 when the company had a share capital of £400,000 and nine vessels at its disposal. Its principal routes at this time were Calcutta—Burma, Calcutta—Singapore, Bombay—Karachi and Bombay—Persian Gulf.

British India can be said to have opened up India, as much of her coastline was unmarked, reefs and shoals uncharted and channels unbuoyed. Officials of the company were responsible for providing all their own navigation aids which included the placing of buoys, marker drums, dredging harbour approaches, building piers and dockside facilities and even constructing make-shift lighthouses.

By 1868 the journey from Glasgow to Calcutta could be made in as little as twenty-seven days which reflects on both the quality of the service and the ships employed on the route. Largely through the efforts of MacKinnon, the company had forged strong links with the Dumbarton yard of William Denny who built many of BI's earlier vessels. That the management of both companies cooperated in designing dual-purpose ships, capable of ferrying large numbers of troops in addition to performing their regular duties, explains why BI secured a substantial share of the lucrative UK—India trooping contract largely at the expense of their rivals, P & O.

The 1870's witnessed continued expansion with several new routes absorbed into the company's schedules including London—Basra (1871), Aden—Zanzibar (1872), UK—East Africa (1873), Zanzibar—Madagascar (1874), a weekly service from Bombay to Basra via Karachi (1875) and the UK—Suez Canal—Colombo—Madras—Calcutta (1876). A period of trooping duty came at the end of the decade when a UK—South Africa service was hurriedly introduced following the outbreak of the Zulu War of 1878-79. By the early 1880's British India's fleet stood at fifty-seven vessels augmented by a further thirteen ships belonging to a subsidiary company, British India Associated Steamers. The latter owed its formation to the award of a mail contract leading to the setting up of a UK—Queensland route with the company's ships voyaging to Brisbane via the Torres Strait. Sadly this expansion was accompanied by a decline in the importance of the firm's Glasgow office and in 1882 the decision was taken to site the company's headquarters in London.

Despite BI's continuing prosperity the worlds of shipping and finance were startled by reports carried in the *Times* newspaper on 23rd May 1914 of a proposed merger between British India and P & O. Both had enjoyed a close trading relationship over the years and their services were complementary; such an amalgamation seemed logical. BI's Chairman, Lord Inchcape, endeavoured to clarify the situation for the investors by emphasising that what was proposed was a merger and not a take-over: "The two companies shall be continued as separate entities, but their interests will become identical". London's financial institutions and the shareholders of both companies expressed approval of the plans and the amalgamation proceeded. At this time British India was the largest individual British shipping line owning 131steamers totalling 598,203 tons (gross) the majority of which provided cargo, passenger and mail services across the Indian Ocean, Persian Gulf and South East Asia, while rarely venturing west of Suez. Fortunately the company livery remained evident on the world's oceans for a further seventy years.

In 1982 the *Dwarka*, the last of the British India's ships in BI line service, was withdrawn and broken up at Karachi leaving only the *Uganda*, a unit of P & O's Passenger Division, to sport the distinctive black funnel with twin bands and BI house flag. She, in turn, was scrapped at Kaohsiung in 1986, despite anguished appeals for her preservation. With her demise the name of British India passed on also.

Burrell and Son

In 1864 George and William Burrell set up business as shipowners, albeit on a rather modest scale. They owned two 70 foot long schooners, the *Janet Houston* and *Jeanie Marshall*, which were designed for use on the Forth and Clyde Canal. Two years later they formed a new partnership with Thomas McLaren and practised as ship and insurance brokers and agents before venturing into deep sea shipping with the *Fitzwilliam*, an iron-hulled steamer, to which was added the *Fitzjames* (1868) and the *Strathclyde* (1871). The latter was built by Blackwood and Gordon of Port Glasgow and destined for the India Trade. It was also the first of many Burrell ships to bear the 'Strath' prefix. By 1875 the fleet had expanded to six vessels operating on Mediterranean routes with the Strathclyde still plying the trade routes to India and a new steamer, the *Strathleven*, about to commence service to China and Australia.

The Clyde Bills of Entry and Shipping Lists for the months of February and March that year indicates the nature of cargoes, trade routes and volume of business enjoyed by the firm:

26th February :

Fitzclarence arrived Glasgow with crew of 18 and cargo of 895 tons of sulphur ore taken on at Huelva and corkwood, wine, seed oil and oranges from Lisbon.

19th March:

Set sail for Gibraltar with 800 tons of coal.

In 1877 the partners amicably agreed to dissolve their partnership leaving William Burrell free to set up a new business enterprise, Burrell and Son, together with a new shipping agency, Burrell and Haig, and a small shipyard, which built puffers, at Hamiltonhill near Port Dundas. Burrell and Son ordered its first steel-hulled vessel from Blackwood and Gordon in 1879. This ship, the *Adria*, was the first of several built for the company over the next seven years. Two of these were jointly owned by Burrell and Son and Schenker and Company of Vienna and operated on the route between Glasgow, Leith and Fiume which proved to be a service of considerable commercial importance.

In February 1880 the company achieved a notable 'first' when the *Strathleven* became the first ship to carry a cargo of refrigerated meat from Australia to the UK. That year also saw Burrell become Glasgow agent for Joseph Hoult's line of steamships trading from Liverpool to the West Indies. The firm later ordered its own vessel, the *Rio Bueno*, for this trade.

By the mid-eighties Burrell ships were conforming to a set pattern with the 'Straths' plying routes to the Far East, the smaller 'Fitzes' operating in the Mediterranean and the *Baltic* and *Rio Bueno* to the Caribbean. The company's houseflag, a blue swallowtail with a red cross formé within a white circle, was becoming a familiar sight on the world's oceans.

William Burrell died on 21st June, 1885 leaving his two sons, George and William (jnr) in control of the family business. Under their guidance the company expanded enormously. George handled the technical specifications of ships and supervised their construction while William ran the commercial and financial aspects of the business. Between 1888 and 1890 orders were placed for ten steel ships with tonnages ranging from 2,271 to 3,265 gross and all fitted with triple expansion engines. These were mainly long-haul vessels designed for the Indian, Chinese and Japanese routes, for liner services, as charters to other companies or for tramping, and included the *Strathdon, Strathdee, Strathearn, Strathendrick* and *Strathblane*. The latter had only just been delivered when she ran aground at the Cape of Good Hope and had to be broken up on the spot. Despite this setback the company continued to thrive, making handsome profits. In 1893 a further twelve steamships were ordered at a time when the shipping industry was in a depressed state. Costs ranged from £39,000 to

£43,000 and all were given 'Strath' names. *Strathgyle* was the largest vessel (5,023 gross tons) and the biggest ship Burrell and Son ever owned. She was fitted with triple expansion engines which drove her at an average speed of 12 knots and was designed for world-wide tramping. In addition the company purchased second-hand ships, all with compound engines.

The new century saw the shipping industry in recession once more, but despite the economic climate the company placed orders for a further twenty steamers with Port Glasgow and Greenock yards. The brothers predicted that the slump would bottom out by the end of 1905. Market slumps enabled the Burrells to obtain ships at rock-bottom prices, the average cost of these new additions to their fleet being £40,000. They entered service during 1906 and 1907 and were followed by a further eight vessels which were delivered in 1909 and 1910, so that by the end of the decade Burrell and Sons' fleet consisted of 34 new steamers. These all conformed to one basic design incorporating all the latest developments in engineering and cargo handling. Each was approximately 4,400 gross tons with an overall length of around 375 feet, a beam of 52 feet, a draught of 25 feet and a cargo capacity of up to 7,150 dwt in a cargo space of 380,000 cubic feet. Cargoes were handled by twelve derricks and ten steam winches. All were equipped with electric lighting and had triple expansion engines capable of an average speed of 12 knots. The *Strathesk(II)* built in 1909 by Greenock and Grangemouth Dockyard was a typical example of the class.

Strathesk

Each ship was operated as a limited company and was manned by British officers with Chinese or Lascar crews. Cargoes varied greatly but mainly consisted of coal, kerosene, grain, cotton, cement, sugar, nitrates, and lumber. Most vessels also featured accommodation for some first class passengers although the standards were far removed from those offered by lines such as Cunard or P & O.

With the rise in market values of ships due to healthier trading conditions during early 1912 and the rise in demand for all types of vessel following the onset of the Great War, the brothers determined to cash in on the situation. Between 1913 and 1916 they sold off virtually their entire fleet. Whether they planned to rebuild after the conflict remains unclear but, in the event, no such scheme materialised. With the return of peace Burrell and Son owned only two vessels, the *Strathearn* and the *Strathlorne*. The former was sold during 1919 but the latter remained with the company until 1930, although a pale reflection of her once proud self. Voyages were repeatedly marked by technical failure and she bore all the signs of neglect. William Burrell was by now devoting much of his time to his vast art collection which prompted one employee, when asked if he was surprised at this, to remark that after experiencing how Burrell ran his ships it was "no bloody wonder that he had got that!"

The firm stayed in business as agents and brokers until 1939. George Burrell died in 1927 leaving William to continue alone until the Second World War. Thereafter he retired to enable him to pursue his art collecting. He died in 1958 having donated his huge art treasury to the City of Glasgow. It is now magnificently displayed as the Burrell Collection in the city's Pollok Park.

The Falls Line Steamship Company Limited

The Falls Line began life as Wright and Breakenridge in 1874 with the firm's headquarters based in Glasgow. It was founded by William Wright and Captain Michael Breakenridge who were both natives of Irvine. Initially the pair confined their interests to the profitable timber trade as the Wright family had a tradition of joinery and cabinet making dating as far back as 1825. Breakenridge was born in 1828 and had spent a lifetime at sea beginning as a cabin boy in 1845 before gaining his masters ticket ten years later. His first command was the brig *Jane* in 1862 and he was to gain much experience handling the large clippers working the North and South American trade routes before retiring to take up a business career. It was he who took the initiative and directed the firm's activities into ship-owning. This decision can be viewed as a logical progression given that the Maritime Provinces of Canada boasted rich sources of timber which were ripe for exploitation. The area was doubly attractive because it was noted for speculative shipbuilding where new vessels, bringing cargoes of timber to the UK, had granted to their British agents the authority to sell the ships as well. For an aspiring shipowner this was a cheap and easy way of acquiring a fleet of ships and commencing trade in one's own right. Later, when iron replaced wood in shipbuilding, the Canadian yards lapsed into decline.

For more than twenty years Wright and Breakenridge went to the Greenock firm of Russell and Company for their vessels. This was probably due to the friendship known to exist between the Russell and Wright families. The most outstanding feature of the company's sailing ships was that all nine vessels were four-masted, six being full-rigged while the rest were barques. Less than 100 four-masters were ever built and all were magnificent examples of the shipbuilder's art, being large, iron-hulled and requiring much manpower to crew them. The Russell yard was noted for the standardisation of hulls and produced a long line of similar-looking sailing ships of which the first two vessels built for Wright and Breakenridge were typical. The *Falls of Clyde* (1878) and the *Falls of Bruar* (1879) were ships of 1,740 gross tons and were both beautiful and elegant. They were followed in 1882 by the *Falls of Afton* and the *Falls of Dee* and the next year by the *Falls of Foyers*. The latter was a fast, heavily-rigged vessel whose career came to an abrupt end early in 1899 when she foundered off the Heligoland Bight with a cargo of nitrate bound for Hamburg, fortunately without loss of life. The *Falls of Earn* (1884) was the firm's largest sailing ship to date with a gross tonnage of 2,292. Like all Wright and Breakenridge vessels she operated as a single ship company (in this case The Ship Falls of Earn Company Limited). On 1st July, 1891 while sailing from Penarth to Sumatra with a cargo of coal, she hove to at Olehleh but swung on her anchor, causing the flukes to penetrate the hull, and sank in 30 feet of water. Despite all efforts to salvage her, she was a total loss.

Almost from the outset the Falls fleet seemed ill-fated and its run of bad luck continued. In the summer of 1886 two iron, four-masted barques - *Falls of Garry* and *Falls of Halladale* - were launched. The former came to grief in February 1898 when her cables parted and she drifted on to a reef at Ichio, New Caledonia although she was salvaged and repaired at considerable cost to her owners. The latter was sold to the Shire Line in 1902 but was lost six years later when she struck a reef in thick fog near Peterborough on the west coast of Victoria, South Australia.

In 1889 the company's first steamship was built. The *Falls of Inversnaid* was a well-decker fitted with quadruple expansion engines supplied by Rankin and Blackmore. A buff funnel with black top was the livery chosen by the line to complement its houseflag (a white banner with blue and red bands at the top and bottom edges). After ten years of service the ship ran aground off Colonia, while on passage to Rio de Janiero, and was badly flooded. She was refloated and underwent extensive repairs before returning to the UK where she was sold to Newcastle owners for £20,250. Six months later she disappeared while carrying a cargo of coal from Newport News to Buenos Aires and was finally posted missing at Lloyds of London on 19th December, 1900.

Shortly after the *Inversnaid*'s completion Breakenridge resigned following a disagreement with Wright over the introduction of steam into the fleet. All his maritime experience was gained during the age of sail and it is quite possible that, like so many old salts, he could not thole this new-fangled source of propulsion. Wright entered into a new partnership with his brother-in-law in 1892 trading under the name Wright, Graham and Company and for the rest of the decade a steady stream of new vessels were ordered of which only one, *Falls of Ettrick* (1894) was a sailing ship. Her career with the firm was short-lived as the decision was taken to dispose of the sailing fleet over a four year period commencing 1898. These were replaced by a succession of spardecked steamers averaging around 5,000 gross tons - *Falls of Bracklinn* (1894); *Falls of Keltie* (1898); *Falls of Lora* (1900); *Falls of Nith* (1907); *Falls of Orchy* (1907) and *Falls of Moness* (1907). In July 1902 the partners decided to place all their vessels under the ownership of a single company.

The single-ship firm 'The Steamship Falls of Keltie Company Limited' was reconstituted and renamed 'The Falls Line Steamship Company Limited' with a share capital of £80,000 and general trading continued as before. Only one other addition was ever made to the fleet and was exceptional in that she never assumed the traditional "Falls" nomenclature, due to wartime restrictions. The vessel was the *Cambrian King* (ex-*Ullapool*) which the firm purchased in 1916. Yet, within a year, the entire fleet was sold off and the partnership of Wright, Graham and Company dissolved in 1919 due principally to lack of business. Fortunately one enduring link with this little-known Glasgow line remains - the *Falls of Clyde* lies preserved in Honolulu, the only survivor of a once proud fleet.

Thomas and James Harrison

Although the names of Thomas and James Harrison and the City of Liverpool remain inextricably linked in the world of maritime trade and commerce, the company forged strong links with Glasgow and the Clyde over many years. Thomas Harrison joined the Liverpool firm of Samuel Brown and Company in 1830 and became a full partner by the end of the decade. The organisation acted as agents for shippers, charterers and ship owners but its principal activity centred on the importation of brandy and fine wines from the Charente area of France. In 1849 brother James was also taken into the partnership and, upon the death of George Brown the son of the founder in 1853, the Harrisons assumed control, renaming the company in the process. Trading as Thomas and James Harrison, the decision was taken from the outset to keep control and ownership in family hands.

The company took delivery of its first iron sailing ship in 1857. She was christened *Philosopher* (1,059 gross tons) and her entry into service heralded the practice of using trades or professions for the naming of vessels owned by the line. In 1861, for reasons of economy, Harrison chose to route the carriage of all spirits through London rather than Liverpool and the steamer *Dragon* was purchased to operate the service, but within months the company faced stiff competition from the General Steam Navigation Company, a much larger enterprise, which undercut the Harrison rate of 25/- per ton and invaded other Harrison preserves by dispatching vessels to Liverpool, Dublin and Glasgow. At this stage the company lost to their rival the valued custom of both Martell and Hennessey forcing them to expand their markets elsewhere. The Indian trade was developed with the appointment of agents in Bombay and Calcutta and a regular service was inaugurated early in 1863 with the sailing vessel *Botanist* (1,160 gross tons). Negotiations with GSNC led to that company pulling out of all provincial routes, in return for which Harrison terminated its London service although calls to Cadiz, for cargoes of Spanish wine, were stepped up. In 1864 the Liverpool-Brazil route was opened followed the next year by intense activity in the Mediterranean fruit

25

trade. 1866 saw the first regular sailing to New Orleans which was initiated by the steamship *Fire Queen* with outward cargoes of cement, and cotton as the main inbound commodity. The opening of the Suez Canal in 1869 allowed the Harrisons to exploit this route and once again it was the *Fire Queen* which made the first transit of the waterway. In the years which followed the company's volume of trade to the Indian sub-continent would increase dramatically. Thus, by the mid-1870's the Charente trade had been eclipsed by other developments, in particular the New Orleans and Iberian peninsula routes.

In 1884 the Charente Steamship Company Limited was formed to take advantage of the newly introduced Limited Liability Law. With a capital of £512,000 and the firm of Thomas and James Harrison acting as managers, twenty-two of the twenty-four vessels owned by the family were transferred to this new commercial entity. Other new routes were established; in 1886 the Belize—British Honduras—New Orleans service commenced with the sole purpose of trans-shipping fruit although this venture was short-lived; the company's influence on the Indian trade increased with the purchase of the Rathbone Brothers' Star Line in 1889 and the subsequent acquisition of their fleet of four steamships; the Harrisons also secured the mail contract for the Caribbean area in 1897 which, although scarcely lucrative, gave them a secure foothold in that part of the world. Routes to South Africa were also scheduled in 1902 after the company joined the South African Conference, and in 1904 Harrison was instrumental in setting up the Conference of West India, Atlantic Steamship Companies. By 1906 the fleet had expanded to 39 ships crewed by 1,876 masters, officers and seamen. The Aberdeen Direct Line (J T Rennie Son and Company) with its fleet of seven vessels was acquired in 1911. These continued to ply the UK-Natal route as before and bore the Rennie livery of grey hull and buff funnel. They also retained their 'In' names, for example, *Inanda, Inkonka* and *Intaba* and from this date all Harrison passenger ships adopted this form of nomenclature. In 1912 the company fleet stood at 55 ships with a further 29 on order but the Great War took a heavy toll on this number with some 27 being lost through enemy action. Harrison partially filled the gap by purchasing twelve units together with the goodwill of the Saint Line (Rankine, Gilmour and Company, Liverpool).

The company's links with Glasgow were further strengthened in 1920 with the purchasing of eight vessels from the Crown Line (Prentice, Service and Henderson). They operated to the West Indies out of the Clyde and all boasted names commencing with the letter 'C' for Crown - *Comedian, Counsellor, Centurion, Candidate, Collegian, Craftsman,* and *Chancellor*. They became a familiar sight on the river during the inter-war years. Five other ships belonging to Scrutton, Sons and Company of London were also acquired and plied the same route.

Like most other lines Harrison experienced economic hardship in the wake of the Wall Street Crash of 1929. In 1931 fifteen ships had to be laid up with ten more being sold at scrap prices the next year. By 1933 the fleet was reduced to forty-one ships but seven units of the International Mercantile Marine's Leyland Line were purchased that year for service to the Gulf of Mexico. Another four vessels were acquired from Furness Withy of which the *Politician* is perhaps the best known. She was stranded on a reef off the island of Eriskay in the Outer Hebrides on 4th February 1941 with a cargo partly consisting of 8 cases of British and Jamaican bank notes and some 275,000 bottles of whisky. The reality proved to be less amusing than Compton MacKenzie's fictional account with several islanders incarcerated for their part in the illegal salvage of some 20,000 bottles of prime-quality Scotch and a major enquiry initiated by the Bank of England some ten years later, after a large volume of the ill-fated currency mysteriously reappeared in Jamaica.

Once again war exacted a terrible price on the Harrison Line with 30 out of 46 vessels sunk by the enemy at a cost of 409 lives. The post-war fleet was initially rebuilt with the purchase of ten Liberty ships and six Empires. Thereafter the emphasis was placed on diesel engined vessels with William Doxford and Sons of Sunderland providing no less than twenty-one of these, so that by the mid-50's the fleet was virtually back to its 1939 strengt, with forty-one units in service and a further two under construction. For forty years ships of the Harrison fleet were instantly recognisable with their distinctive silhouettes, their tall funnels proudly bearing three bands, two white separated by a red on a black background, and their immaculate standards of maintenance. In 1951 the first real profile changes took place with the appearance of the *Astronomer* which had 3 hatches positioned forward of her island superstructure. She was a shelter decker and was followed by 15 similar vessels. The *Adventurer* of 1961 introduced the final Harrison profile. Her engines were placed aft allowing for more cargo space amidships where the largest hatches were also to be found. A 180 ton Stulcken derrick facilitated heavy cargo handling.

Although eager to place orders for vessels with British shipyards, Harrison was forced by British shipbuilding's uncompetitiveness and subsequent decline in the 1960's to seek new tonnage elsewhere. In 1970 the company chose to diversify into the bulk and container trade and placed orders for three ships (all bulk carriers) with Japanese yards during 1973. These vessels were the *Wanderer, Wayfarer* and *Warrior* all of 16,317 gross tons. That year Harrison formed a consortium with HAPAG-Lloyd, KNSM and Cie Generale Maritime et Financiere called the Caribbean Overseas Line (CAROL) and orders were placed with a Polish yard for six container ships. Up till now CAROL has offered a weekly service to a multitude of destinations including Hamburg, Bremerhaven, Amsterdam, Antwerp, Tilbury, Le Havre, Liverpool, Barbados, Trinidad, Aruba, Curacao, Puerto Rico, Dominican Republic, Haiti, Jamaica, Guatemala and Honduras with feeder services to lesser ports like Belize.

Thomas Law and Company: The Shire Line

The Shire Line was founded by Thomas Law during the 1860's and until the turn of the century consisted entirely of a fleet of handsome sailing vessels operating regular services to Australia and New Zealand. Literally thousands of Scots used Shire Line ships to emigrate to the Antipodes with each ship laden with cargoes for the journey home.

In 1907 the company's owners resolved to add their first steamship to their existing fleet of 20 vessels. Whereas all of these carried 'shire' names, a different style of nomenclature was adopted for the steam-powered units. The first of these to be introduced into service was the *Largo Law*, a vessel of 3,974 gross tons whose career lasted for some twenty five years. Four years later a second ship, the *Berwick Law* (4,680 gross tons), joined the fleet as consort to her older sister with additional tonnage being purchased second hand in 1912. This was the *Duns Law* (ex-*Port Chalmers*), a vessel of 4,077 gross tons which had previously been owned by the Port Line. All three ships sported a funnel livery practically identical to that of the Nelson Line and flew the Thomas Law houseflag, a white diagonal cross on a red background.

The Great War took a heavy toll of company vessels and virtually decimated the sailing fleet, though as late as 1922 two were still in service. Of the steamers, the *Duns Law* was seized by the Germans in

August 1914 while berthed at Hamburg. When she returned to her owners at the end of hostilities, she was almost immediately sold. The *Berwick Law* was less fortunate having been torpedoed and sunk by a U-boat some 22 miles west of Cape Tenes on 2nd December 1917, a fate which the *Largo Law* narrowly escaped on two occasions.

The company continued to buy second-hand tonnage in the decade following the signing of the Versailles Treaty of 1919. The 1908 German prize *Wotan* was pressed into service as running mate to *Largo Law* but lasted only a year with her new owners before being sold off. Her replacement too bore the name *Duns Law* but dated back to 1906 when she was launched as the *Irismere* for the firm of G Jaques of Newcastle. This ship of 3,690 gross tons remained with Thomas Law and Company for the next nine years before being sold to Italian owners in 1929.

Further second-hand tonnage was acquired in 1923 and at two yearly intervals until 1927 when the *Misty Law* (ex Holland-America Line's *Zuiderdijk* of 1912), *Cowden Law* (ex *Raeburn* and Verel Line's *Scottish Monarch* of 1918) and *Berwick Law (II)* (ex Prince Line's *Roman Prince* of 1914) joined the fleet. Thereafter the company adopted a policy of ordering new tonnage, the first of which was the *Lammer Law* in 1929 (4,971 gross tons), designed to replace the ageing *Duns Law*. This was followed in 1930 by the *Traprain Law* (4,973 gross tons) which superseded *Misty Law*; the service of both new ships was brief for they were sold in 1932. *Lammer Law* was ultimately sold to Soc.Garibaldi of Genoa. She was at Pearl Harbour when the Japanese bombed the US fleet in 1941 and when America declared war against the Axis powers her crew promptly scuttled her. *Traprain Law* became the property of the Donaldson Line and was subsequently torpedoed in the North Atlantic on 9th May 1941.

These sales left the Laws with only two remaining vessels, the *Cowden Law* and *Berwick Law* and they too were sold off in 1933. The latter passed on to Greek ownership and was wrecked off Cape Barbas in June 1936 while the former, somewhat surprisingly, flying the Greek flag but with a Shanghai registry, was seized by the Japanese in 1941. She operated as the *Urato Maru* until sunk by the allies in October 1944.

Although the company had no fleet after 1933 it remained in existence for a further fourteen years relying entirely on chartering to continue trading. With the death of the last surviving partner in March 1947 the affairs of Thomas Law and Company were finally wound up.

The Clyde Shipyards

Barclay, Curle and Company Limited
Stobcross, Clydeholm, Whiteinch

It was in 1818 that John Barclay established a shipyard at Stobcross for the purpose of building and repairing small sailing vessels. The slip was capable of lifting ships of up to 200 tons although this was later increased to 400 after extensive reconstruction. It was left to Barclay's son, Robert, to expand the business and set up facilities exclusively for repair work which proved a source of considerable income for the rapidly growing firm.

In 1845 he formed a partnership with Robert Curle and James Hamilton and two years later John Ferguson was appointed yard manager. From this point there was a shift in emphasis as the last named set about establishing iron shipbuilding in the yard and the company's fortunes soared. One of the most notable vessels of this period was the *City of Glasgow* (1848) which weighed in at over 500 tons and was one of the Clyde's largest ships to date. In 1855 the firm moved to larger premises at Whiteinch taking over the Clydeholm yard of J G Lawrie and the following year two new partners joined the business, Andrew McLean and Archibald Gilchrist, the latter a well-known Clydeside name. By 1857 an independent engine works had been established on the recently acquired site while further expansion occurred in 1861 with the purchase of the old Finnieston Cotton Spinning and Print Works. The ageing buildings were levelled and replaced by an engine shop offering every up-to-date facility. From 1863 the firm began trading under the name of Barclay, Curle and Company. Eleven years later the decision was taken to sell the Stobcross site to the Clyde Trustees who required it for the building of Queen's Dock, yet it was those same Trustees who prevented Barclay, Curle's further expansion, which would have included new ship-repairing facilities, by refusing to allow the work to proceed in the early months of 1878.

In 1884 the firm was registered as a limited company and continued to prosper. It purchased repair works in Whitefield Road, Govan in 1902 and operations were further extended in 1912 with the acquisition of the Elderslie shipyard and dry docks from John Shearer and Son. That year also saw the beginning of a change in ownership

31

for Barclay, Curle and Company Limited. The Tyneside yard of Swan Hunter and Wigham Richardson became the principal shareholder and would ultimately control more than 99% of the business. The shipyard continued to grow, acquiring the North British Engine Company at Scotstoun in 1912 and the Whiteinch and Jordanvale shipyards in 1923. The former was an asset of some importance. Barclay, Curle's main claim to fame lay principally with its engine works which had moved in 1894 to the engine shop in Finnieston Street with the boiler works sited in Kelvinhaugh Street but ultimately everything was transferred to the North British plant. The emphasis thereafter was on the fabrication of oil engines. In 1911 the company had produced Britain's first ocean-going motorship, *Jutlandia*, for the East Asiatic Company of Copenhagen and was to continue its pioneering work with diesels although, as was the case with the McLaggan engine, not always successfully.

The construction of marine engines and boilers gave Barclay, Curle and Company a worldwide reputation for excellence and their ship repair business was only marginally less important. Evidence of this can be found in the firm's First World War repairing statistics: 2,244 vessels repaired afloat, 999 vessels in drydock. As the years went by this side of the company's business was run down and finally closed in 1974 when the drydocks were handed over to Yarrow Shipbuilders.

Redgauntlet

There can be no doubt that Barclay, Curle and Company ranks among the great names in Clyde shipbuilding. In all some 750 vessels slid down the ways. From 1870 on these were principally cargo-passenger ships for the Indian and Far Eastern services or intermediate liners for the Atlantic routes. Links with many notable shipping lines were formed; these included the British India Line, Castle Line, Ben Line, Donaldson Line and P & O. It is almost impossible to draw up a list of the company's more distinguished products without making omissions but few would dispute the inclusion of the following: *Grandtully Castle* (1879/Castle Line); *Redgauntlet* (1895/North British); *City of Paris* (1907/City Line); *Morea* (1908/P & O); *Elephanta* (1911/British India) and, from a later period, the troopships *Dunera* (1937) and *Nevasa* (1955) and the school cruise ship *Uganda* (1952), all for British India.

William Beardmore and Company Limited
Govan, Dalmuir

William Beardmore assumed control of his father's Parkhead Forge in 1879 and within the space of twenty years had developed it into one of the leading steelworks of the day. A keen entrepreneur, he was quick to identify the expanding market for ships, engineering products and armour plating created by the Anglo-German arms race and determined to carve for himself a share of the profits. To this end he purchased the bankrupt shipyard of Robert Napier which provided him with an entree into a new market and guaranteed a secure outlet for the products of the Parkhead Forge. The purchase price was £200,000 and operations began under the new ownership in 1900. After a period of some five years Beardmore decided to move to a site which would afford his company greater room for expansion. He chose Dalmuir on the north bank of the Clyde and proceeded to build a yard capable of handling the heaviest class of work. A wet dock was excavated and 80,000 cubic feet of wood was sunk into the foreshore to form 6 berths. Huge engine and boiler works were constructed together with an enormous gantry to cover the longest ships. The Dalmuir Naval Construction Works as it was known opened in 1906 and shortly after, on 22 June, received its first Admiralty contract. This was for the Lord Nelson class battleship *HMS Agamemnon*. However Beardmore, in an effort to create the country's most up-to-date and best equipped shipyard, had overstretched himself financially. This, together with his other market dealings, forced him to seek amalgamation with the English-based firms of Vickers and Son and Maxim Limited. Ultimately Vickers would have a 50% stake in the company.

Unlike the Napier yard which built all manner of vessels, Beardmore was essentially an armament and armour plating concern with a shipbuilding facility attached to it where the accent was on building capital ships. To begin with orders were scarce, principally because Beardmore himself had no proven track record in the shipbuilding field. It was not until 1909 that the Admiralty placed another order with the company for the Dreadnought *HMS Centurion*. There followed a boom period lasting four years in which three seven thousand tonners were built for the Adelaide Steamship Company, together with the Dreadnoughts *Benbow* and *Ramilles*, two destroyers and three light cruisers, with more orders to come. Despite this the yard failed to show a profit because production costs were higher than in other yards. Losses for the period 1912-1914 totalled £357,043, but Parkhead Forge continued to make huge profits from its iron and steel forgings and the yard was kept in operation by cross-subsidising.

The Beardmore organisation played a major role in the First World War, manufacturing a wide range of products including aeroplanes, airships, artillery, submarines and armour plating. However, it was this very diversification which proved detrimental to the Dalmuir shipyard which only received Admiralty contracts for four destroyers, one cruiser and two submarines during 1915, with a repeat of this order the following year. Dalmuir was seen primarily as an engineering centre for gun mountings and the like, rather than as a place for building ships. The yard's fortunes picked up in 1917 due to a change in Government policy forced by the naval crisis brought on by the success of Germany's U-Boats. Lost tonnage had to be replaced and so, by November 1918, Beardmore had built sxty-nine ships totalling 118,089 tons, made profits of around £500,000 and invested £800,000 on facilities tailored to meet wartime requirements.

This growth continued in the immediate post-war era. £400,000 was spent on expanding the Dalmuir engine works to enable it to manufacture large steam turbines, while a further £250,000 was provided for laying out three new berths and plate-working sheds for the construction of tankers and tramps. Orders were confirmed for eight vessels including the *Lancastria* (ex-*Tyrrhenia*) for Cunard, *Cameronia* for the Anchor Line and the *Conte Rosso* and *Conte Verde* for Lloyd-Saboudo of Genoa. Unfortunately the boom period was short-lived. The 20's saw a severe depression in the shipbuilding industry generally with Beardmore being hit particularly hard. Management had encouraged diversification into locomotive building as the wartime heavy plant and machinery installations were especially suited to this. The scheme was ill-conceived as this market had insufficient work to support existing builders let alone new ones, while the declining fortunes of the airship industry presented the firm with yet another financial setback. Outstanding among the factors leading to the company's ultimate collapse however, was the management's strategy for dealing with production bottlenecks. Where these occurred and made output difficult to maintain they simply bought-over firms to get them out of the immediate crisis. By the early 20's some of these acquisitions had not recovered their initial purchasing cost, forcing the parent company deeper into the red.

The Washington Naval Treaty of December 1921 led the British Government to cancel orders for three battle-cruisers one of which had been earmarked for Dalmuir. Beardmore was placed in the unenviable position of having to accept any orders it could get including tugs, hoppers and motor yachts, all of which were built on slips designed for capital ships. 1926 was a particularly bad year for the yard when only two orders were received, one for a sludge boat and the other for a cargo-passenger motor ship, *Itope*, for Brazil. The following year orders were placed by the Admiralty for one cruiser and two submarines, but thereafter few vessels were built at Dalmuir. On 9th September 1930 the impending closure of the yard was announced. The last ship to be launched from Beardmore's yard was the *Pole Star* built for the Commissioners of Northern Lighthouses. In all 170 vessels were built there over a period of 30 years.

Among the notable products of this great shipyard, in addition to those mentioned above, were the Allan liner *Alsatian* (1913), Lloyd Saboudo's *Conte Biancomano* (1924) and the Latvian ice-breaker *Krisjanis Valdemars* (1925).

Blythswood Shipbuilding Company
Scotstoun

The Blythswood Shipbuilding Company Ltd was co-founded by Hugh MacMillan, an ex-general manager of the Fairfield yard, and Donald Bremner, formerly of John Brown and Company. In the wake of the Great War the two decided to enter the shipbuilding market as the demand for replacement tonnage for war losses was high, and the yard commenced trading in 1919 on a site adjacent to Yarrow and Company at Scotstoun in Glasgow. The newly-established firm embarked on its shipbuilding activities with Ship No.2 entered in the order book because Macmillan laid a fictitious keel to show that the yard had experience and was a going concern. Its first product was the tanker *British Architect* closely followed by a series of cargo vessels for the Furness Withy service to the west coast of South America. These were known as the 'Pacific Enterprise' Class.

The Blythswood yard placed emphasis on the need for economical construction technique applied to standard-type vessels incorporating attractive lines and in this respect was keenly alert to the advantages of well-researched sales promotion. It produced ships of quality and reliability at a reasonable price and consequently demand was high.

Perhaps Blythswood's most celebrated vessel was the tanker *San Demetrio* built in 1938 for the Eagle Oil Company. She was attacked in November 1940 while on convoy duty in the North Atlantic and set on fire. Her crew took to the lifeboats but the ship stubbornly refused to sink and was ultimately reboarded by 17 members of her company who brought her home with most of her cargo of petrol intact. The *San Demetrio*'s reprieve was short-lived however, as she succumbed to a U-boat attack some two years later.

After Hugh MacMillan's death in 1957 the firm seemed to lose its impetus and ceased trading in 1964 during a decade which saw shipbuilding and marine technology become increasingly more sophisticated and in which the Blythswood company, with its basic approach to ship construction, could find no role to play. The yard completed its last vessel only days before closure. The *Fingal* had been ordered by the Commissioners of the Northern Lighthouses and was a very fine ship and a fitting tribute to the ailing company. This smart, all-purpose, seaworthy vessel is based at the Scottish west coast port of Oban. Despite 25 years of service she remains well-maintained in her attractive livery of navy-blue hull with nicely proportioned light-brown funnel and white upperworks. At the time of writing however her future is in some doubt as she is now surplus to CNL's requirements and has been shortlisted for disposal.

The Blythswood Shipbuilding Company was sold to the Norcross organisation in 1964 but within twelve months Yarrow was in control and today the yard forms part of their extensive complex at Scotstoun.

During its forty-five years existence no less than 140 vessels were launched, the majority of which were tankers, and all bore the Blythswood hallmark of quality.

Charles Connell and Company
Scotstoun

Charles Connell had served his apprenticeship as a shipwright with Robert Steele and Company before becoming manager in the Kelvinhaugh shipyard of Alexander Stephen and Son. In 1861 he decided to strike out on his own and established a yard in Scotstoun where the initial emphasis was on the construction of sailing ships, mostly for the China trade. These included the clippers *Taitsing* and *Spindrift*. For over one hundred years the firm continued to function under the control of the Connell family, producing over 500 vessels but, unlike other yards, it had no facility for fabricating marine engines, this work having to be sub-contracted out to other engineering firms. Over the years the yard built up good relations with several owners including T and J Harrison of Liverpool, Brocklebank's, Wilhelm Wilhelmson, the Ben Line, James Nourse of London, Patrick Henderson and the Inman Line for whom they built the large cargo-passenger ship *City of Chicago* in 1883. The Nourse connection proved especially rewarding. This company ordered no less than 20 sailing ships from the yard each with a specific trade in mind, such as grain bulk carriers or nitrate carriers. Of this number, five were exceptionally large ships and included the *Mersey* of 1894. Relations with the Edinburgh-based Ben Line also proved profitable. By 1964 a total of forty-eight ships had been built for the company by Connell's and included such outstanding vessels as the steam turbine ship *Ben Loyal* of 1959 and the motor vessel *Ben Ledi* (1964). These were two of the fastest merchant ships on the Far East route affording stiff competition for the company's rivals the Glen Line.

If Connell's reputation was built on his yard's ability to produce first class sailing ships this is not how his company is remembered today. The First World War established the future pattern of production for the yard with the emphasis on the construction of easily produced and inexpensive cargo vessels, a role which other yards such as D & W Henderson would follow. High standards of workmanship were maintained which enhanced the firm's reputation for producing vessels of quality.

Within the yard itself management—worker relations were excellent. While most owners commanded respect, this was not always coupled with popularity. Successive generations of the Connell family 'knew' their employees and were aware of their circumstances. The yard may not have been the biggest but it was one of the happiest, with an ever-mobile shipyard population eager to work there. An especially attractive feature was the unique bonus system operated by the firm. Upon the receipt of a contract each trade would elect a committee, usually comprising a shop steward, assistant steward and three tradesmen. This committee would negotiate with management to work out a price for all the work undertaken by that particular trade on the vessel. If, for example, the trade was joinery, each committee member kept a detailed note of the time worked by every joiner in his section. All amended work or alterations were regarded as extra time and charged accordingly together with ordinary hours plus overtime. This formed the basis of the weekly pay-packet without bonuses. When the ship was completed however, all the joiners' hours were totalled and the grand sum was subtracted from the agreed contract price. What remained was divided by the sum of the total hours worked by that trade and each man was paid a bonus, determined by this hourly rate, for the time he had worked on the vessel.

Throughout its long history the Connell yard was only idle for six years between 1931 to 1937, a time of general recession in the industry. In 1968 the firm passed out of the family's control into the Upper Clyde Shipbuilders' Consortium, effectively removing another familiar name from the Clyde shipbuilding scene.

A & J Inglis
Pointhouse

Anthony Inglis was a bellhanger, smith and gas fitter to trade who took the decision to expand his business interests in 1841 to include shipsmithing and machine fabricating. This aspect of his work did moderately well but it was not until 1847 when he went into partnership with his brother John, a marine engineer, that the firm really began to prosper. Within a short time they had set themselves up as boilermakers at the Whitehall Foundry in Anderston and in 1850 produced the machinery for the paddle tug *Clyde*. The company's reputation for the quality and reliability of its marine engines continued to grow, reaching a peak in 1855 when it was awarded the contract to provide the power source for the *Tasmanian*. The *Tasmanian*, one of the largest and fastest ships of the day, was a remarkable vessel of 2956 gross tons and sister to the slightly smaller *Australasian*. Both were extremely powerful and were capable of sustaining a steady 11 knots under steam alone. They each had accommodation for 200 First and 60 Second Class passengers. It was only a matter of time before the brothers opened their own shipyard at Pointhouse on the basin of the River Kelvin. The yard commenced business in 1862. It had a patent slipway and a marine railway which allowed for the movement of hulls around the yard and enabled them to be unslipped slowly into the river. Normal berths were constructed for conventional launchings and were angled to the water so that vessels were launched in the direction of the mouth of the Kelvin. Among the first ships to be built at the Inglis yard was the *Erl King* which inaugurated the route from the UK to Shanghai via the Cape of Good Hope in the mid-1860s. Around this time Anthony's son, John, joined the firm and proved himself a useful asset. His marriage to a member of the Denny family afforded him numerous useful contacts which he and his father were only too eager to exploit. In time he would become a director of the North British Railway Company which, with the expansion of the Clyde coastal shipping market, was to place no less than 13 orders for passenger steamers with the firm. Anthony Inglis, the firm's founder, died in 1884 and there can be no clearer indication of his success as shipbuilder than the estate he left behind after 22 years in the business. It totalled over £152,000 which, in terms of today's monetary values, would have made him a multi-millionaire.

On average the yard produced five vessels a year and forged close links with several shipping lines, in particular British India for whom no less than 53 ships were built prior to 1914. However, the company's forte was the construction of private yachts of which there were several outstanding examples. The *Alexandra* of 1907 was built for King Edward VII as the Royal Yacht. She was a triple screw vessel powered by Parsons steam turbines and most elegant and imposing sight. The *Safa-el-Bar* built for the Khedive of Egypt in 1894 used the more conventional reciprocating machinery but was no less aesthetically appealing.

In 1919 John Inglis sold the shipyard to the Harland and Wolff group of Belfast. The post-war slump was hitting British shipbuilders hard and, unsure of what the future might hold, he decided to call it a day. Despite this change in ownership, the Pointhouse yard continued to function under its old name for a further 43 years before final closure in 1962. Over the years it produced many fine ships including the *Norman Court* (1869), a clipper which in six out of seven years beginning in 1870 made better time on the China tea run than the better known *Cutty Sark*; the *Cosmos* (1879) a paddle steamer built for South American owners which was the first Clyde-built ship to be fitted with electric light; the iron hulled full-rigger *Loch Etive* (1878), built to trade with Australia and remaining on British Registry for 32 years which, at one point, had author Joseph Conrad as third mate; the *PS Kenilworth* (1891) for North British Railways; NBR'S *Waverley* (1899) and her successor built for LNER in 1947, both notable additions to the Clyde's coastal cruising fleet; the *Talisman* (1935) the diesel-electric paddle steamer which served her owners for over 30 years and was the Mulberry Harbour HQ ship during the Normandy landings of 1944; the *Prince Edward* (1911) and the *Maid of the Loch* (1953) both long-serving members of the Loch Lomond fleet.

PS Kenilworth

Russell & Company Limited, Lithgows Limited
Port Glasgow and Greenock

In 1874 Joseph Russell, Anderson Rodger and William T Lithgow entered into partnership and purchased the Bay shipyard from Messrs McFadyen of Port Glasgow which they then operated under the trade name of Russell and Company. It was the firm's policy from the outset to supply large sailing ships for the long routes to South America and the Pacific, as steamships were not economically viable on these. Although clippers were fast they were expensive to run so the partners opted for slower, roomier vessels which were built to a standard design and more easily maintained. This proved so successful that by 1879 the company was forced to look for additional premises to undertake the construction of these carriers. They leased a second yard at Cartsdyke in the east end of Greenock and three years later, in 1882, purchased the Kingston yard at Port Glasgow which was to become the largest shipyard on the lower Clyde. It was during the 80's that William Lithgow decided to reform the company's financial structure by reducing charges and costs. His solution to the problem was to build standardised vessels in anticipation of a quick sale. In the event that no buyer could be found, Lithgow floated a company to manage the ships himself. During the period 1882-92 a total of 271 ships were built, putting the yard at the head of Clyde production for a decade. Lithgow's reforms help to explain this success.

In 1891 the firm's founders amicably agreed to dissolve the partnership. Russell retired while Rodger assumed control of the Bay yard leaving Lithgow the sole remaining partner. He continued to build standard ships but there was a change of emphasis. The age of sail was almost over and Lithgow was aware of it. Future production would concentrate on tramp steamers and small cargo carriers. Among the yard's regular customers were the Bank Line, Nourse, Burrell and Bruugaard Kiosterud of Dramen.

William Lithgow died in 1908 leaving an estate valued at over £1 million. His sons, James and Henry, inherited the business and continued to run it most efficiently, purchasing back the Bay yard in 1912 and that of Robert Duncan in 1915. It is somewhat surprising that the name of Lithgow, the business enterprise, was unheard of until 1918 when Lithgows Limited was established, for even after the partnership of 1891 had been dissolved the company had continued to trade under Russell's name. With the ending of the Great War the new company emerged to face a bright and dynamic future.

The Lithgows were outstanding businessmen, shrewd and ambitious, with a desire to provide employment for the depressed areas on Clydeside. At no time was the yard idle while they were at the helm. During World War One ships with a total gross tonnage of 315,141 were launched and a staggering 1,200,000 tons in the Second World War, the greatest tonnage of any British shipbuilder of the time. From 1919—1929 1.8% of world tonnage came from the Lithgow yards. This rose during the depression years of 1932—1934 to 5.3% on average, and in 1934 their output alone accounted for 61.8% of all Clyde tonnage. The inter-war years also saw an increase in the number of firms coming under Lithgow's control. These included James Dunlop (steel stockist), the North British Welding Company (in 1936) and, most outstanding of all, the acquisition of the Fairfield Shipyard in 1935.

As was the case with so many Clyde yards Lithgows experienced a decline in its fortunes in the post-war period. Customers remained loyal, but only for a time. Foreign competition resulting in lower prices and quicker delivery dates took its toll as did the development of air freight transport. The writing was on the wall and in 1969 the decision was taken to merge both Lithgow's and Scott's in a policy of rationalisation designed to ensure survival. Another of the great Clyde yards had entered the history books.

Throughout their long histories Russell and Lithgows produced some outstanding vessels including the *Falls of Dee* (1882) which made a record passage for a full-rigged sailing ship from New South Wales to Chile in 1909; the *Hinemoa* (1890) an early refrigerated ship which competed favourably with the clippers; the *Maria Rickmers* (1891) a heavily-rigged sailing ship of 3,822 tons, the largest sailing ship in the world at the time, which left Saigon with a cargo of rice on 14th July 1892 and was never seen again; the *Brilliant* (1901) an oil carrying sailing ship capable of transporting 6,000 tons deadweight.

Tod and MacGregor
Meadowside

David Tod and John MacGregor, both engineers, formed a trading partnership in 1834. They gained considerable managerial expertise whilst working for Robert Napier and determined to follow in his footsteps. In 1836 they opened a shipyard near Mavisbank Quay and for the next eleven years concentrated on the construction of iron-hulled vessels before acquiring a further site at the mouth of the River Kelvin. Mavisbank was then sold to the Clyde Trustees. In its comparatively short life the yard produced some fine ships including the Clyde paddle steamer *Loch Goil* (engined by Napier) and the iron screw yacht *Vesta*, a schooner-rigged steamer some 110 feet in length. The latter's construction is known to have presented problems for the builders, for on her completion David Tod wrote in a letter to her owners, "I hope you will not bring us any more screw boats - we prefer paddle steamers." Despite this remark the firm continued to build propeller-driven vessels culminating in the magnificent *City of Glasgow*, built in 1850 for the Inman Line of Liverpool. The *City of Glasgow* has been called the true prototype of the modern ocean steamship. She was 270 feet in length with a beam of 33 feet and propelled by a two-bladed screw. The vessel offered accommodation for 52 first and 85 second class passengers with further capacity for 400 people travelling steerage. The emigrant paid 8 guineas (£8.40) for his passage, in return for which he got a numbered berth and plain but adequate meals usually comprising porridge, beef, fish and plum pudding on Sundays. William Inman owed his success to the emigrant trade for he offered the traveller passage in conditions which were the exception rather than the rule in the 1850's and 60's. This efficient and well-designed ship was capable of running on the North Atlantic without need for government subsidy. Sadly her career was short lived for she sailed from Liverpool in 1854 en route to New York with 480 passengers and crew aboard and was never seen or heard of again. Despite her fate the Board of Directors of the Inman Line recognised that she had been a profitable ship of novel layout and strong construction, and time after time the company returned to Tod and MacGregor for new tonnage.

On 28th January 1858 the yard opened Glasgow's first dry dock at its Meadowside site. Its dimensions were staggering for the time, being 160 yards long, 21 yards wide at the entrance and 18 feet deep at high spring tides. During its first year of operation 30 ships totalling 20,000 tons were stemmed there.

The company also pioneered under-cover working conditions by having two vast sheds built over the building berths. Although the structures were pulled down in the wake of violent storms, they were the first of their type in Scotland and heralded a practice which today is regarded as commonplace.

The firm's dynamism emanated principally from David Tod and his death in 1859 was a setback for the yard. It continued to function however, receiving orders over the next 14 years from P & O, Inman and Cunard, who had their iron-screw steamship *Cuba* built there in 1864. There was regular income too from the Clyde and coastal shipping companies, many of whose vessels were purchased by the Confederacy as blockade runners during the American Civil War (1861-65) and who were forced to order replacements with some of the huge profits made on these transactions. The end was in sight

43

however, for by the early 70's the order books were far from full, a state of affairs hard to comprehend given that Clyde shipbuilding was at its zenith. The final blow came in 1873 when the Inman Line placed an order for a North Atlantic liner with a Birkenhead yard. Tod and MacGregor was put up for sale as a going concern for £200,000 and shortly after purchased by David and William Henderson and the Anchor Line.

In addition to those vessels referred to above the following products of Tod and MacGregor are worthy of mention: the *Inverary Castle* (1839), and *Mary Jane*, later *Glencoe* (1846). There can be no better testament to Clyde shipbuilding than these two ships, both of which continued to ply the Clyde and West Highland routes, the former till the 1890's and the latter till 1931.

Inverary Castle

D & W Henderson
Meadowside

With the collapse of Tod and MacGregor the site, together with Thomas Seath's old yard, was purchased by David and William Henderson in 1873. The new firm had strong connections with the Anchor Line from whom it derived much ship repair and building work. Marine engines were already being fabricated at the company's Finnieston works but the acquisition of these new premises allowed for the construction of hulls as well. For many years the yard was known colloquially as the 'Anchor Line' by the citizens of Glasgow. Its product range was extremely varied and included over the years everything from tugs and tenders to sturdy cargo ships and sleek

44

ocean liners. From 1882 to 1916 Henderson's benefitted from the skills of George Thomson, a naval architect of distinction, who specialised in yacht and sailing craft design of which the five masted sailing barque *France* remains an outstanding example. She was built in 1890 for Bordes et Cie. of Dunkirk and was capable of carrying 6,200 tons of nitrates, giving her a greater cargo-handling capacity than any other vessel engaged in the same trade. Thomson's racing yachts made the Henderson name a by-word in this exclusive market and included the yachts *Valkyrie II* and *III* and King Edward VII's *Britannia*. The America's Cup contender *Thistle* was also built there although designed by G L Watson.

During the First World War the yard built merchant ships to a standard design of 8000 tons deadweight and all fitted with triple expansion engines giving a speed of around 11 knots. After hostilities had ended trade fell away and orders became fewer, forcing the yard to accept contracts well below the amount which other yards would be prepared to offer. With the collapse of the Anchor Line in 1935 the shipyard was compelled to cease trading and the workforce was paid off. Harland and Wolff purchased the company's ship repair assets and goodwill thus ensuring that the Henderson name would survive for a few more years. However, Harland and Wolff's rationalisation policy of the early 60's sounded the death-knell for the firm whose name finally disappeared from the Clyde scene in 1962. In its latter years it had suffered from lack of investment and in the post-war age of rapidly advancing technology its outmoded and exhausted capital equipment meant higher costs and hence prices, coupled with longer delivery dates. In a highly competitive market the Henderson yard was a non-starter.

Ivanhoe

45

When a shipyard's demise is a slow one it is easy to forget the high points and achievements of an earlier age. There can be no doubt that Henderson's contribution to Clyde shipbuilding was enormous with many of its vessels becoming household names of their time. The following list highlights but a few: the *Ivanhoe* (1880/Firth of Clyde Steam Packet Company), *Lord of the Isles* (1891/Glasgow and Inverary Steam Packet Company), and the *Columbia* (1902), *Circassia* (1903), *Caledonia* (1905), *Elysia* (1908) and *Cameronia* (1911), all built for the Anchor Line.

Harland and Wolff Limited
Govan

Harland and Wolff's Clydeside operations took second place to those of the company's principal yard at Queen's Island, Belfast. The firm was founded in 1859 by Edward J Harland from Tyneside and Liverpool businessman G C Schwabe. G W Wolff was placed in charge of the drawing office but was later taken into partnership in January 1862. The yard prospered due to the energy and enterprise of its directors together with the high class of work it turned out. Relationships with major shipping lines were established, including the Bibby Line and Thomas Ismay's White Star Line for whom Harland and Wolff produced some of the most elegant, stylish and superbly built vessels ever to leave a shipyard. These included the *Oceanic* (1899), White Star's 'Big Four' *Celtic, Cedric, Baltic* and *Adriatic* (1901-1907) and the ill-starred Olympic Class comprising *Olympic, Titanic* and *Britannic* (1910-1913).

Much of the firm's success was due to W J Pirrie (later Lord Pirrie) who was admitted to the partnership in 1874 and ultimately became Chairman of Harland and Wolff Limited. It was he who was at the helm when the company reached its peak of success in the early years of the twentieth century and who took the decision to expand Harland and Wolff's operations on the Clyde. In 1912 the firm purchased three adjacent Govan sites including Robert Napier's old yard and proceeded to construct an integrated steel fabrication and engineering ship factory complete with hammerhead cranes which became a Clydeside showpiece. The yard produced a wide range of vessels during its fifty year history ranging from Royal Navy monitors in 1915 to tankers and cargo ships which proved to be its basic workload. With the passage of time Harland and Wolff's influence on the river grew, with Belfast ultimately controlling Caird and Company (1916-36), Harland and Wolff (Irvine) Limited (1914-1915), D & W Henderson (1935-1962), A MacMillan and Sons Limited (1920-1930) and A & J Inglis Limited (1919-1962). In addition to this a number of engineering firms were incorporated into the group.

After the Second World War the yard went into decline as the effects of the 30's recession began to be felt. Little investment took place despite heavy wartime commitments and with ships increasing greatly in size in the post-war era the yard was drastically in need of modernisation. Berths required widening and lengthening and ageing tools and equipment needed to be replaced. In 1962 Harland and Wolff (Belfast) announced that the yard would be closed with all future shipbuilding activity confined to Queen's Island. Inglis' yard was disposed of as was D & W Henderson's drydock. Alexander Stephen acquired the outfitting basin for ship repair work while the rest of the site was put up for sale.

Over the years the yard produced a varied range of well-constructed craft including: the *Highland Hope* (1930), a passenger motorship, for the Nelson Line; the beautiful turbine steamer *Duchess of Hamilton* (1932) for LMS Railway's Clyde fleet; the tanker *British Trust* (1937) and the Norwegian heavy lift ship *Belisland* (1962).

Duchess of Hamilton

47

Glasgow's Docklands

The deepening of the River Clyde was only the first step towards establishing Glasgow as a major seaport and commercial centre. Although a link with the sea had been forged it still remained for adequate facilities to be provided for the loading and discharging of cargoes. In time this became the responsibility of the Clyde Trustees who made provision for the construction of riverside quays and off-river tidal basins and docks. A short history of the city's dockland development is outlined in *Better by Yards*.

Essential to a well-designed, efficient dock system at the turn of the century was the availability of canting basins, goods sheds, a variety of lifting equipment and access points for railway transport, each catering for a wide range of contrasting markets from the prestigious ocean liner trade to the carriers of general-purpose cargo. The latter occupied much of the available dock space, handling such diverse cargoes as steel, heavy engineering plant and equipment and railway locomotives all destined for foreign parts and imports of coal, iron ore, timber, grain, fruit, cotton and phosphates for home consumption. To handle such products sometimes required the construction of specialised facilities such as Clydebank's Rothesay Dock, purpose-built at the turn of the century to meet the needs of the coal and iron ore markets both of which experienced rapid growth during the 1890's. In the case of coal, shipments doubled from $1\frac{1}{4}$ to $2\frac{1}{2}$ million tons per year between 1892 and 1898, much of it being re-exported. Rothesay Dock alone shipped 1.6 million tons in 1916 with an annual tonnage for the port of Glasgow in excess of 4.2 million tons. Accommodation was provided for other specialised cargoes. Merklands Quay was designed to handle livestock imports from Canada, Ireland and the West Highlands while a major granary was erected at Meadowside to accommodate up to 20,000 tons of grain in 150 separate silos; the city's other principal docks (Queen's, Prince's and King George V) all functioned as general cargo terminals.

The maintenance of dock facilities was the responsibility of a number of related bodies. Most important of these was the conservancy authority known as the Clyde Navigation Trust which was responsible for maintaining the port's approach channels. This could involve dredging, surveying the tideway, preventing pollution, lighting and buoying wrecks, shoals or other underwater obstacles and removing these where possible. The Clyde Pilotage Authority worked closely with this body providing pilotage for ships travelling to and from Glasgow Harbour. A master could entrust his vessel to the pilot until it was safely docked or in open sea. With the increasing volume of river traffic came a corresponding growth in the roles played by the customs and emigration authorities while the late-nineteenth century mass-migrations both to and from the city highlighted the need for a port health authority as well. As large ports were frequently the focus for organised criminal activity, a river police force also became a necessity. Add to this numerous public and private wharfingers, lighterage and towage firms, a dock labour board, stevedores and master porters, shipping companies, brokers and forwarding agents together with an effective transport network all of whose requirements impinged on the design and operation of the dock system and Glasgow's dockland in its heyday is revealed as a complex, bustling entity. The city's importance as a centre of mercantile commerce can be measured by the number of shipping lines whose vessels regularly berthed there.

Dock and Cargo Handling

It was not until the 1830's that Glasgow's reputation as the West of Scotland's principal seaport began to be established. Prior to that date the city was inaccessible from the sea due to the shallowness of the Clyde and it took over 100 years of dredging, widening and deepening to create the international waterway which became known throughout the world. When Cunard's greatest liner to date, the *Aquitania* made her way downstream from John Brown's Clydebank yard in June 1914 she sailed over areas that people had walked on 150 years earlier.

In the 18th Century Glasgow's merchants were dependent on Clyde harbours further down the Firth handling their cargoes. Greenock was one, while its neighbour, Port Glasgow, was specifically created to meet the demands of the city's ever-increasing ranks of entrepreneurs. Even so, neither could offer more than the most basic of cargo handling facilities. All loading and discharging was undertaken using only manual tackle and an army of cheap labour. The absence of storage space meant that cargoes were unloaded on to the dockside and lay exposed to the elements where they were also the target of widespread thievery. It was left to the merchants to arrange for transportation to the city's warehouses. These men were a thoroughly different breed from their 20th century counterparts. Erratic voyage times enabled many of them not only to import and export but also to act as brokers, agents, bankers, underwriters, and shipowners, frequently operating from the quayside or in Glasgow's Trongate at the "Plainstanes" (a primitive form of stock exchange). Principal trading commodities included bales of silk, bags of cotton, barrels of rum, puncheons of palm oil, casks of ginger, frails of figs, firkins of tallow and hogsheads of tobacco. But, regardless of the nature of the cargo, all had to be manhandled. Some progress was made during the early 19th century. Warehouses were provided along with a variety of manually operated hoists and treadmill cranes worked by gangs of men; yardarm rigs, winches and ships' derricks were also available to facilitate handling. In 1846, at Newcastle Quay, William Armstrong built the country's first hydraulic dockside crane which was capable of lifting heavier loads more efficiently than the older-fashioned methods, but this was slow to catch on as such machinery was expensive to install and manual hoists were cheaper to operate given the vast pool of labour at the disposal of merchant and shipowner. This reluctance to modernise the dockland infrastructure and machinery plagued the industry right up to the 1870's and eventually played a major part in the closure of many docks.

It was the change from sail to steam which had the most far-reaching impact on the dock landscape. Originally, when the need for warehousing had been recognised, most ports like London, Liverpool and Hull constructed acres upon acres of multi-storey goods sheds hard to their quay edges. With the appearance of iron-hulled steam cargo vessels however, quick turn-arounds were necessary to offset their building costs and thus reduce the periods of time when they were not earning. This became more feasible once railway networks developed and steamship schedules became regularised. Ships assisted with the discharge and loading by their own steam-driven gear but, as a consequence of these changes, warehouses became redundant as there was no longer any need for long-term storage. Worse still, these buildings proved to be physically obstructive since their location provided little room for cargo-handling. This problem did not manifest itself to any extent once Glasgow became established as a major port, for here single-storey transit sheds were the norm and not the high-rise warehouses which were so common at an earlier period in other ports. The reason for this was that the city's docks acted as a rapid-transit servicing centre for the Scottish Highlands and Islands. In time other ports would follow Glasgow's example by having similar facilities with numerous dockside openings and planned railway links as integral parts of the network.

The aftermath of World War Two saw the development of bulk handling techniques and this too had an impact. The traditional dockside sheds were quite useless for bulk cargoes as some of these, like oil, sulphur, gas and wine required no buildings of any description, merely pipelines, although grain continued to be an exception. The trend towards open-space dockside facilities continued into the 1960s with the introduction of containerisation. Container terminals featured little in the way of warehousing as they were rapid-transit cargo processing centres. The containers themselves obviated any need for storage as the duration of their stay on the quayside was minimal. Such terminals were characterised by mobile gantry cranes of varying capacities equipped to unload the specially designed sea-to-land container ships whose cargoes were then trans-shipped by road or rail from the quayside. Greenock's Princes Pier became the Clyde's principal container terminal in 1969 and by March 1973 there were some thirteen different services operating to the United States and Canada including those of the Johnson Line, Seatrain Lines, ACL and Hapag Lloyd.

View from the Finnieston Crane

Such change effectively caused a drastic reduction in the size of the dock labour force which fiercely opposed these measures, without success. Containerisation meant a quicker turnaround and was thus more cost-effective; losses by theft and damage were minimalised and fewer ships were required. Worse still, from Glasgow's viewpoint, selected ports in the UK became container terminals for specific routes. The south of England became the reception centre for the Australian, New Zealand and Far Eastern Services and effectively severed the city's cargo-liner connections with these countries. In 1966 the city's general cargo trade with Australia totalled 100,000 tons. Ten years later it was non-existent. Containerisation, together with Glasgow's decline as a mercantile centre, had all but eliminated the docker from the Clyde scene.

Monuments to Iron and Steel

The Port of Glasgow has a twelve foot tidal range and, at one time, boasted four tidal docks. Three of these, Kingston, Queen's Dock and Prince's, were completed in the 19th century while the fourth, King George V, was opened in 1931. Open docks were satisfactory where there was an adequate depth of water over the dock sills. In general, where gates were necessary, that is where there was considerable variation between high and low water marks or at the entrance to dry docks, these often marked a place in the network where water had to be crossed and so pedestrian, road and railway bridges became a common dockland sight. Examples of these could be found in many harbours in England but were much less evident in Glasgow. Nevertheless the city featured some outstanding structures in iron and steel ranging from manual and hydraulic bridges to swing and bascule ones.

Pre-eminent among Scottish bridgebuilders at this time was Sir William Arrol whose company was founded in 1868 and prospered until the years before the Great War. If one monument to his achievement were to be singled out it would surely be the magnificent Forth Railway Bridge of the 1880's. Weighing over 51,000 tons it was the heaviest bridge in Britain and a triumph of Victorian engineering. Arrol was also involved in the erection of the new Tay Railway Bridge, following the collapse of Thomas Bouch's earlier construction in December 1879. His contribution to late-nineteenth century Glasgow included the construction in 1875 of a 700 foot, seven span lattice bridge over the Clyde and the Caledonian Railway Bridge linking the city's Central Station with the south side of the river. Within the context of dockland he left another enduring legacy: a variety of lifting gear ranging from small, mobile hydraulic cranes designed for cargo handling to the massive 180 ton hammer headed monsters used by some of the major shipyards like Brown and Fairfield. Cranes of this

A. McKAY 1989

55

type were introduced in the early years of the century to handle boilers, low speed steam turbines and parts of reciprocating engines which could weigh upwards of 100 tons. Similar cranes of more modest proportions replaced the old-style sheerlegs which were a familiar sight until the end of the century.

Working in the Docks

At the beginning of the twentieth century the dock labour force constituted one of the largest pools of casual employment in the country. It is estimated that some 10,000 men were employed on an irregular basis within the bounds of Glasgow Harbour alone. Despite the availability of labour-saving devices designed to facilitate cargo handling, this type of work was highly labour intensive and involved the man-handling of anything from crates, bales, barrels and live-stock to heavy engineering plant and equipment. Such work carried with it an element of risk and injuries were commonplace with little or no legislation in existence governing safety standards. Accidents aboard ship were most frequent during the first few days of employment. This could be due to inexperience, the aftermath of a long spell of illness or where the worker had experienced prolonged unemployment leading to near starvation. Sheer willpower saw a man through the working day and his financial reward at the end of the week would have totalled no more than 15/- (75p). To survive the workforce had to be young and strong.

Within the workforce three distinct classes could be identified. At the top end were the watermen and lightermen whose job it was to load and navigate the barges, scows and lighters employed in the off-loading of cargoes from vessels. They represented the skilled element within the labour force and were a well-organised body. An apprenticeship system was operated which allowed them to function as a closed-shop and thus control their numbers. Given the era in which they worked their wage levels were good, with an average take home pay of around £2 to £3 per week, although to earn this a man had to work all hours of the day or night.

Beneath them in the class structure were the stevedores who worked in gangs and whose job was to load and unload cargoes from visiting ships. They liaised directly with the shipowners' agents, not the dock officials, and were therefore involved in the wage negotiation process. Their work was regular and reasonably well-paid with weekly earnings of around £1 16/- (£1.80p).

56

The remaining dock workers made up the biggest single group. Known simply as 'dockers' they helped to unload ships. Their work was unskilled but could require great reserves of strength. Since the work was of a casual nature dockers came from diverse sections of the working class including shoemakers, ironturners, plumbers, painters, joiners, bakers and clerks or any trades where short-time prevailed. Bakers, for example, were employed by the job, not the week, with most of their work being done at night. In the daytime they had a chance of a job in the dock at any hour and were especially experienced in handling flour and grain cargoes. Clerks on the other hand were only useful for light work such as checking-off cargoes as they came into the dock warehouses or sorting them out prior to loading.

Much of the dockers' waking hours were spent queuing for the chance of securing another spell of back-breaking work. Success depended on a number of factors: the time of year, the weather and the availability of work within other industries in the region. One union leader penned a vivid description of how men were picked for work:

We were driven into a shed, iron-barred from end to end, outside which a contractor or foreman walked up and down with the air of a dealer in a cattle market, picking and choosing from a crowd of men, who, in their eagerness to obtain employment trample each other underfoot, and where like beasts they fight for a chance of a day's work. Such struggling, shouting, crushing. Then one man, younger than the rest, would throw himself bodily at the head of this close-packed struggling mass, for what? The possession of a ticket which at best would afford four hours labour for no more than 6d (2¹/₂p) an hour.

Calls for workers were made at different intervals during the day. These were usually 7am, 8am, 8.45am and 12.45pm. Those who were not chosen had to kill time as best they could, in all weathers, until the next call. Dockers tended to take employment depending on the type of vessel, and here three sub-classes of worker could be identified - Grain Men, General Labourers and Metal Men. The first specialised in the unloading of grain and flour carrying ships while the second handled mixed cargoes. The Metal Men earned the highest wage for the hardest work with an hourly rate of 7d (3¹/₂ p). They worked exclusively on the coal and ore carriers and a large number of them had connections with the iron trades. It was almost impossible for general labourers to gain access to this branch of dock work which was a closed-shop in all but name. Grain Men could earn anything up to

12/- (60p) per day but the work was exhausting and could not be sustained throughout the week. The average weekly wage varied from around 20/- (£1) to 24/- (£1.20p) depending on the season, with employment paid by the hour and the job. General labourers earned 5d (2p) per hour with an average weekly wage of between 15/- (75p) and 18/- (90p). Night work paid 1d extra and was much sought after.

Several of the major shipping lines, and in particular the Allan, State and Anchor companies, employed foremen whose job entailed the selection of the general labour force. The Clan Line was the exception, preferring to contract work with the stevedores who, in turn, employed men to work under them. The stevedores, who could earn as much as £20 per week, were a formidable group with the power to hire and fire at will.

The general public's view of the dock labourer was of a thriftless, improvident and frequently drunken individual completely lacking in self-respect. Many married dockers lived with their families in the Plantation district of the city but, for the majority of the unattached, home was one of Glasgow's model lodging houses. Having no social or domestic ties they spent a fraction of their income on the bare necessities of life and the rest on prostitutes and bad whisky. A fair number spent some period of their existence in the Poor House. The Governor of one such establishment (Barnhill) stated in a report on poor relief in 1908 that the previous June had seen 418 persons admitted of which 373 came from model lodging houses and 401 stated that the cause of their application was drink. More than half those given assistance came from the city's dock labour force.

The dockers' low public esteem was aggravated by the archaic system of payment to which they were subject. Matters came to a head over this in June 1889 when a series of strikes were instigated. The particular cause of the dispute was the nightly pay system. This was flawed insofar as a docker never had more than a few shillings in his possession at any one time because he was paid by the hour and the job. The strikers wanted to be paid once or even twice a week to allow their money to accumulate. When the employers refused to comply with their wishes the dockers withdrew their labour, forcing management to recruit its workforce elsewhere. This 'blackleg' labour became the object of vicious intimidation. Foremen were attacked and severely beaten while workers had to be brought in by fleets of tugs to avoid the hail of stones which greeted them when they tried to gain access through the dock gates. At one point the Allan Line's terminal at Prince's Dock was virtually under a state of siege with over 600 men engaged in the loading and discharging of cargoes whilst several thousand chanted, threatened and jeered from beyond the perimeter fence.

The campaign of intimidation proved ultimately successful as the dock management and shipping lines found it increasingly difficult to recruit labour of any description. With strike funds exhausted the labour force returned to work but in a much better bargaining position than before. They adopted a go-slow policy which, within weeks, forced the employers to negotiate and a wage increase of $1/_2$d per hour on the prevailing rate of 5d was secured. The dispute had been a hostile and violent one partly due to the divisions between the different classes of dock worker over pay and conditions and the sectarian bitterness known to exist between the rival groups.

Unrest continued into the first decade of the new century culminating in the national dock strike of 1911 which was not fully resolved until the end of the Great War. However, the events of 1889 were directly responsible for the setting up of the Glasgow Dock Labour Union with an initial membership of 1,500. This was superseded ten years later by the National Union of Dock Labourers, also founded in Glasgow.

It was this body which finally persuaded the Government to set up an enquiry into wages and conditions of employment in the dock labouring industry. When it reported its findings in 1920 the following recommendations were made:

1. That a national minimum standard wage of 16/- (80p) per day be established on the basis of a national agreement for a 44 hour week.

2. That the registration of dock labour be introduced into all ports, docks and harbours in the United Kingdom.

3. That all wages were to be paid weekly.

In Glasgow this was implemented as follows:

Working Hours	8am—5pm Monday to Friday
	8am—12 noon Saturday
	12 noon—1pm lunch
Nightshift	6pm—4am
	10pm—11pm Supper

59

Special rates were paid for handling certain cargoes and an additional 4p extra was on offer for those who chose to work through their lunch break. These rates did not survive long as the depression of the 1920's caused high unemployment and enabled employers to reduce wage rates once more. The ill-feeling this engendered lasted well into the post-war era and relations between management and workers remained uneasy and fraught with suspicion. It also had the effect of creating one of the tightest 'closed shop' unions in the country with a reputation for militancy which even the wartime boom failed to modify.

Changes in cargo-handling techniques in the early 1960's exacted a high price from the dockers' unions and much reduced their effectiveness. The implementation of containerisation was chiefly to blame for the mass redundancies which followed, so that today this commercial sector survives only as a pale shadow of its former self.

Clyde-Built

Given the considerable number of noteable vessels launched from the Clyde over the last 150 years, the selection of a mere thirty is a daunting task. The careers of some of the truly great names such as the *Queen Mary, Aquitania, Lusitania* and *Empress of Britain*, were outlined in *Better By Yards*. In the following chapter the choice is somewhat freeranging, encompassing the meek as well as the mighty.

Tonnages and Complements

Figures for tonnages and passenger complements are based on those issued by the shipping lines upon commencement of service. Gross tonnages are quoted throughout.

Company Liveries

Funnel colours are given first, followed by hull colours in italics.

Allan Line: Red with black top, separated by a white band; *Black, red underbody and white waterline*

Anchor: Black; *Black with red waterline*

Bibby Line: Salmon pink with black top; *black hull, red waterline*

Blue Funnel: Light blue, black top; *Black, red waterline*

British India: Black with two white bands; *Black, red underbody*

Canadian Pacific: Buff yellow, black top on earlier ships; *Black, red underbody with white waterline on earlier ships*

Cunard: Red/black top and stay rings; *Black, red underbody and white waterline*

Donaldson: Black with white band; *Black, red water line*

Elder Dempster: Buff yellow; *Black, red waterline*

Harrison: Black with a red band separated by two white bands; *black, red waterline*

Inman: Black with white band; *Black, red waterline*

New Zealand Shipping Co: Yellow; *Black, red underbody and white waterline*

P & O: Black; *Black with white band, red waterline*

Royal Holland Lloyd: Buff with black band; *Black with white trim and red underbody*

Swedish-America: Yellow with blue disc encircling three gold crowns; *White with blue underbody*

Union-Castle: Red with black tops; *lavender grey , red waterline*

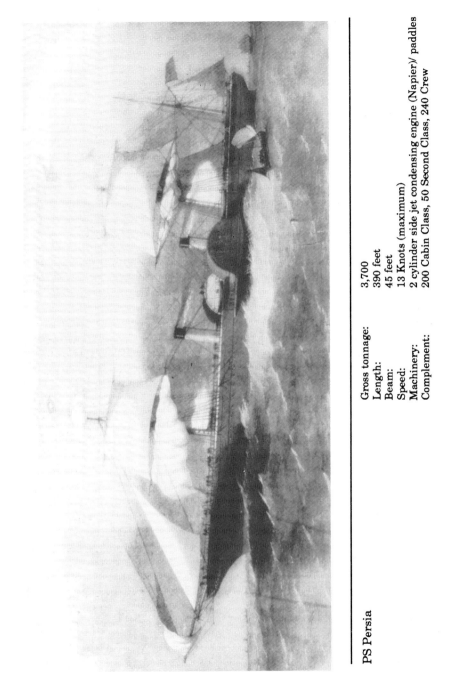

PS Persia

Gross tonnage:	3,700
Length:	390 feet
Beam:	45 feet
Speed:	13 Knots (maximum)
Machinery:	2 cylinder side jet condensing engine (Napier)/ paddles
Complement:	200 Cabin Class, 50 Second Class, 240 Crew

PS Persia, 1856 (Cunard Line)

The *Persia* was originally ordered by the Cunard Line from William Denny and Brothers of Dumbarton but, due to a serious miscalculation in estimating the contract price, the yard begged to be released from its commitment and the order was placed with Robert Napier's yard instead. The vessel was launched on 3rd July 1855 and undertook her trials on 8th January the next year. The *Persia* was the longest vessel afloat at the time as well as being the first iron-hulled transatlantic liner. She was also the most expensive, having cost over £130,000 to build, a far cry from the £43,512 estimate submitted by Denny. The price was justified however as the ship proved to be one of the most successful liners operated by the Cunard Line in addition to being a stunningly beautiful vessel. She had two well-proportioned funnels placed fore and aft of her heavily-gilded paddle boxes, an elegant clipper bow, sleek eliptical counter stern and, in accordance with the prevailing needs of the time, carried acres of canvas on the yards of her sturdy twin barque-rigged masts. The *Persia* was little short of a masterpiece. On 26th January 1856 she embarked on her maiden voyage to New York. On this crossing she collided with an iceberg, but the damage was superficial and she reached her destination safely. Her rival, the *Pacific*, which belonged to the American Collins Line, was not so fortunate. She had left Liverpool the day before the *Persia* and sailed into oblivion. It was this ship that the Cunard flier had been designed to beat and thus regain the transatlantic speed record for Great Britain. The fate of the *Pacific* has never been determined for not a body, lifeboat or scrap of wreckage was ever found. Some six months after her maiden voyage the *Persia* took the

Blue Riband with an Atlantic crossing lasting 9 days, 1 hour and 45 minutes, a record she held until 1862. To sustain her at this speed required a fuel consumption of 143 tons of coal per day and, in a career spanning some twelve years, she made well over 300 crossings. The *Persia* was requisitioned as a troopship in 1861 and ferried several army regiments to Canada during the period of tension between Britain and the USA (Unionist North) in the wake of the Trent incident, but thereafter she returned to commercial service on the North Atlantic. Her short life was now almost at an end. She was sold to J R Thomson for the sum of £10,000, a fraction of her building cost, and suffered the indignity of having her powerful engines removed. Later, in July that year, she was purchased by William McArthur and Matthew Wilson of Glasgow who in turn sold her to J Moss and Company in January 1871. Although laid-up for much of the time the *Persia* found another buyer when she became the property of S N & A Castle in February 1872 but she never sailed again and made her final trip to the breakers before the year was out.

SS Servia, 1881 (Cunard Line)

Gross tonnage:	7,391
Length:	515 feet
Beam:	52.1 feet
Speed:	16 Knots (maximum)
Machinery:	3 cylinder compound engine (Thomson)/single screw
Complement:	480 First Class, 500 Third Class, 252 Crew

The *Servia* was launched from the yard of J & G Thomson at Clydebank on 1st March 1881. It was Cunard's intention to name her *Sahara* but this was changed shortly before the vessel was completed.

The *Servia* was the only Cunarder to be designed on the Bibby principle, that is length ten times beam, and cost £256,903 to build. In some ways she was an innovative ship; she was fabricated in mild steel and fitted throughout with electric lighting which had yet to become standard practice on Atlantic liners. At the time of her launch she was the world's largest vessel after Brunel's *Great Eastern* and must be regarded as one of the most stylish and elegant ships of her time. A crack was discovered in her shaft prior to undertaking her trials and this delayed her maiden voyage to New York by several weeks. She embarked on her first crossing on 26th November and was an immediate success. At this stage in her career she had no boat deck and her lifeboats were on projecting skids. She was steered from beneath the poop whalebacking right aft and was barque-rigged with topgallant masts.

The *Servia*'s career was not without incident. In 1891 she had to be towed into New York after her shaft had snapped and the following year she collided with the American sailing ship *Undaunted* although neither ship sustained serious damage. On 7th June 1893 she ran down the sailing barque *A McCallum*, fortunately without loss of life. Her winter refit that year saw the addition of a boat deck and it is in this final form that she is illustrated above; her accommodation was also extensively remodelled at this time. In November 1899 she became *HMT 31* for Boer War trooping, being chartered by the British Government for 21/- per ton per month. On 9th June 1900 she resumed her Atlantic service to New York but after more than a year, was withdrawn by Cunard and replaced by the *Ivernia* in September 1901. Thereafter she was laid-up until January 1902 when she was sold to Thomas W Ward for £15,625. The ship was then stripped to a hulk at Barrow-in-Furness before being towed to Preston for demolition.

TSS City of New York, 1888 (Inman Line)

Few would disagree that the sisters *City of New York* and *City of Paris* were among the most beautiful vessels ever built. They combined all the elegance, flair and style of the nineteenth century with the travelling public's ever-increasing demands for speed. Each ship had a long, slim hull, attractive counter stern and heavily gilded clipper bow. A low superstructure was topped by three closely-spaced and well raked stacks bearing the colours of the Inman Line. Forward of the bridge was an enormous glass roof which crowned the Victorian splendour of the First Class Dining Saloon below. Both vessels

TSS City of New York

Gross tonnage:	10,499
Length:	560 feet
Beam:	63.2 feet
Speed:	21 knots (maximum)
Machinery:	Triple expansion engines/twin screw
Complement:	540 First Class, 200 Second Class, 1,000 Steerage

sported three masts which added to the impression of speed and urgency.

The *City of New York* was the first of the two to be launched, on 15th October 1888, some seven months before her sister. Both were products of the J & G Thomson Yard in Glasgow. The *New York* undertook her maiden voyage from Liverpool to New York on 1st August 1888 and almost four years later to the day captured the Blue Riband for a record voyage from Sandy Hook to Queenstown at an average speed of 20.11 knots. Between them the *New York* and the *Paris* vied for supremacy on the North Atlantic with the White Star record breakers *Majestic* and *Teutonic*. However, the efforts of all four vessels proved unequal to the performance of the Cunard sisters *Campania* and *Lucania* when they made their appearance in 1893.

City of Paris after alterations

Under the Inman Flag the *City of New York* enjoyed some five years of uninterrupted service but the early nineties were a time of economic hardship for the Inman Line and by 1892 the ailing firm was on the point of bankruptcy. Both ships were put up for sale and subsequently went to the highest bidder, the American Line. They were renamed *New York* and *Paris* and had their passenger capacities reclassified. The *New York*'s first voyage for her new owners commenced on 11th March 1893 when she left Southampton bound for New York on which route she continued to operate for the next five years before being called-up for service with the US Navy as an auxilliary cruiser in the Spanish-American War. For the duration she was rechristened *Harvard* but reverted to her previous name upon the cessation of hostilities. In May 1901 she was withdrawn from the

North Atlantic roster and sent to the Cramp shipyard in Philadelphia for extensive refitting which included a new set of triple expansion engines and two new funnels instead of the original three. Although still a fine ship her balanced lines had been marred by these alterations. Her sister shared a similar fate being given a new set of quadruple expansion engines and twin funnels of greater girth. In 1913 the *New York*'s passenger accommodation was rebuilt with no First Class and the following year she entered service on the New York-Liverpool route in the wake of the outbreak of war. When America joined the Allies in 1917 this splendid liner was again conscripted for duties as an armed transport. Her second mast was removed and her name changed to *Plattsburg*. She performed in this role until 1919 when she was handed back to the American Line. As the *New York* she undertook her first voyage from New York to Southampton in February 1920 but was laid-up in November that year. She was purchased by the Polish Navigation Company of New York in 1921 and sailed under their houseflag for the first time on 14th September with a voyage from New York to Danzig. Her route was changed the next year when she undertook a spell on the New-York Mediterranean run before being sent to the breakers in Genoa in 1923.

The *New York* enjoyed thirty-five years of trouble-free service during which time she and her sister became legends on the North Atlantic. The romance of the ocean liner was diminished by their passing.

TSS Saxonia, 1899 (Cunard Line)

The *Saxonia* was one of a pair of ships ordered by the Cunard Line for the North Atlantic route. She was built by John Brown and Company of Clydebank while her sister, *Ivernia*, was the product of the Swan & Hunter yard on the Tyne. Each boasted the tallest funnels ever installed in a Cunard liner or indeed any ship up to that time and were truly magnificent vessels in every respect. Both possessed smart, well-balanced profiles featuring a straight stem, elliptical stern, four tall perfectly raked masts which complemented the tall pencil-slim funnel rising nearly 100 feet from the boat deck and a low, centrally-placed superstructure. *Saxonia* could be identified by the ventilator derricks on her foredeck, a feature absent in her sister. Internally both ships were masterpieces of design, the First Class Dining Saloon being particularly outstanding in the Clyde-built ship.

68

Gross tonnage:	13,799
Length:	600 feet
Beam:	64.9 feet
Speed:	16.8 Knots (maximum)
Machinery:	Quadruple expansion engines (Wallsend Slipway)/twin screw
Complement:	164 First Class, 200 Second Class, 1,600 Steerage

TSS Saxonia

The *Saxonia* was launched on 16th December 1899 and undertook her maiden voyage to Boston on 22nd May 1900. She remained on this route until 1911 when she was transfered to the Trieste to Boston service. This early part of her career was uneventful, the exception being October 1909 when she answered a distress call from the Hamburg-Amerika liner *Scotia* which had suffered a broken shaft. *Saxonia* towed the stricken vessel some 170 miles to the Azores. In 1912 she was transferred once more, this time to the Fiume-New York route and her passenger accommodation altered so that she became a Second Class and Steerage ship. On 29th August 1914 she sailed for New York from the port of Liverpool and then on to Quebec for modification as a troop transport. She returned to her home port with a full complement of some 3,000 Canadian troops but was withdrawn and spent the next nine months on the Thames as a prisoner-of-war ship. In May 1915 she was on the Liverpool—New York service once more. During this time *Saxonia* occasionally acted as a troopship. However, her role in this capacity was dramatically increased from March 1917 when she was acquired under the Liner-Requisition Scheme and by April, with the entry of the USA into the war, she embarked on a punishing schedule ferrying American doughboys eastbound. With the return of peace *Saxonia* resumed the Liverpool —New York service on 25th January 1919 but switched to the London route on 14th May. The next year she was refitted at Tilbury and had her funnel shortened by 16 feet in the process. When she re-entered service she operated to New York out of London although Hamburg became her eastern terminal on occasion. For the next four years she continued to ply the Atlantic but by the mid-twenties she was something of a curiosity, a Victorian relic lost in the vibrant, liberated jazz age where there was no place for her. Cunard decided to withdraw *Saxonia* from service in November 1924. She was laid-up at the Tilbury buoy for four months before being sold for £47,000 and broken up at Hendrik Ido Ambacht.

TSS Cassandra, 1906 (Donaldson Line)

Gross tonnage:	8,135
Length:	455 feet
Beam:	53.2 feet
Speed:	15 Knots (maximum)
Machinery:	Triple expansion engines (Scott's)/twin screw
Complement:	250 Cabin Class, 950 Steerage

The *Cassandra*, although a Donaldson ship, was registered in the name of Cassandra Steamship Company, a concern managed by the parent firm. She was launched from Scott's Shipbuilding and Engineering yard at Greenock on 27th June 1906 and was the first major passenger liner built for the Donaldson fleet, at a cost of £111,184, a modest sum even for those days.

The ship embarked from Glasgow on her maiden voyage to Montreal on 22nd September that year and proved herself to be a reliable vessel and an asset to the company. If any criticism could be levelled at her it was that she was found to be rather a wet ship forward on the west-bound crossings as she butted into the prevailing headwinds. The *Saturnia* (1910) and *Letitia* (1912) were both modelled on *Cassandra*'s design but this fault was corrected by fitting a more traditional North-Atlantic forecastle to each ship capable of withstanding the rigors of the ocean's weather. *Cassandra* was fast enough to enable her to complete the round trip to Canada in 28 days (16 days at sea and 6 days at either Glasgow or Montreal) but this time was further reduced by two days when the Clyde Navigation Trust installed a coal-loading crane at her Glasgow terminal which allowed her to coal without the necessity of moving. From 1914 to 1918 she continued in service, for the most part carrying cargoes of meat to the Clyde but a brief interruption to this routine came in 1915 when she was enlisted to take part in the Dardanelles and Gallipoli campaigns.

With the formation of the Anchor-Donaldson Line in 1916 she was transferred to its ownership and operated for the company until 20th November 1924 when she undertook her last passenger sailing to Portland, Maine. On her return *Cassandra* underwent conversion as a cargo-only carrier and inherited a new name, *Carmia*, the next year.

Her days with Donaldson ended on 24th December 1929 when she was sold to the Red Star Line and as the *Drachenstein* was employed carrying uncrated Ford cars to Europe. By 1934 Red Star was in financial difficulty and the board of management took the decision to scrap the ship. Her final voyage came in April when she sailed for Germany and the breakers' yard.

TSS California, 1907 (Anchor Line)

Gross tonnage:	8,669
Length:	470 feet
Beam:	58.3 feet
Speed:	16 Knots (maximum)
Machinery:	Triple expansion engines (Henderson)/twin screw
Complement:	232 First Class, 248 Second Class, 734 Third Class

The *California* was launched from the yard of D & W Henderson on the 9th July 1907. She had been ordered by the Anchor Line for their Glasgow—New York route and undertook her maiden voyage on 10th October that year. She was a good-looking ship having a straight stem and hull of the three-island type with counter stern. Her twin stacks were well-spaced and raked giving her a finely balanced appearance. *California*'s early career on the North Atlantic passed without incident until 28th June 1914 when she ran aground in fog on Tory Island off the north coast of Ireland. Her salvage was only completed by 20th August following which she was towed to Glasgow for repairs. These took a further 14 months due to the extent of the damage to her plating and the wartime shortages of steel. The Anchor Line were forced to charter other vessels, mainly from Cunard, to meet the demands of her transatlantic schedule. *California* re-entered service in October 1915 and continued to ply between Glasgow and New York until 29th January 1917. That day she departed her American terminal en route to Scotland. Nine days later, on 7th February at 9.10am, she was struck by an enemy torpedo aft of her central superstructure and began to sink rapidly. Within seven minutes the ship was gone, taking with her forty-three out of her total complement of 205 passengers. Her captain was one of the survivors. As tradition dictated he was the last man to leave the stricken vessel and was sucked down when the ship took its final plunge. Her boilers then exploded and he was blown to the surface, rescued and after a brief period of recuperation, returned to duty with the Anchor Line.

TSS Grampian, 1907 (Allan Line)

Gross tonnage:	9,603
Length:	502 feet
Beam:	60.2 feet
Speed:	15.8 Knots (maximum)
Machinery:	Triple expansion engines (Stephens)/twin screw
Complement:	210 First Class, 250 Second Class, 1,000 Third Class

Among the largest of the Allan Line's vessels to sail from Glasgow to Canada during the first decade of the twentieth century was the *Grampian*. She was built in 1907 by Alexander Stephen and Sons at Linthouse and was one of a quintet of new ships built for the company between 1904 and 1907, the others being *Victorian, Virginian, Corsican* and *Hesperian*.

The *Grampian* was launched on 25th July 1907 and completed by the following December whereupon she undertook her maiden voyage from Glasgow to Montreal and performed most successfully. Initially

73

she weighed in below 10,000 tons gross mark, but subsequent revisions in her tonnage figure meant that by 1910 she was registered at Lloyd's as a vessel of 10,947 tons gross.

At the outbreak of war in 1914 she remained on the Canadian route although operating on a reduced schedule. Unlike her sisters *Victorian, Virginian* and *Corsican* she was never employed on active service either as a troopship or armed merchant cruiser but she shared the fate of all Allan Line ships when Canadian Pacific bought the Glasgow-based company on 1st October 1915. Her career with her new owners was short-lived, for in March 1921 she caught fire while berthed at Antwerp and became a total loss. Four years later her charred hull and superstructure was sold for breaking up to F Rijsdijk, Hendrik-Ido-Ambacht.

TSS Orcoma, 1908 (Pacific Steam Navigation Co)

Gross tonnage:	11,553
Length:	530 feet
Beam:	62.2 feet
Speed:	17 Knots (maximum)
Machinery:	Quadruple expansion engines (Beardmore)/twin screw
Complement:	250 First Class, 200 Second Class, 100 Third Class, 600 Steerage

The *Orcoma* was a product of the William Beardmore yard at Dalmuir. She was launched on 2nd April 1908 and entered service for the Pacific Steam Navigation Company on 27th August that same year operating on the Liverpool-Magellan-South American west coast route. She was a sturdy vessel and the fastest operating in that part of the globe. In 1909 she took the first Thomas Cook tour to South

America at a cost of £300 per passenger and five years later distinguished herself by taking the outward-bound record from Liverpool to Callao via the Straits of Magellan in a time of 32 days 22 hours and 40 minutes including ports of call. She returned to the UK in November 1914 with an even faster time, and narrowly missed being involved in the destruction of Craddock's British cruiser squadron at the Battle of the Coronel. In March 1915 *Orcoma* served as an armed merchant cruiser on the Northern Patrol with the 10th Cruiser Squadron and was finally de-commissioned on 7th November 1919. She reverted to PSNC service on her original route which she continued to ply for the next four years before being temporarily withdrawn to enable her to undergo extensive refitting. This included conversion to oil-firing and the modernisation of her passenger accommodation. *Orcoma* continued in service for a further 10 years before being sold to Hughes, Bolckow & Company for the sum of £14,580. In June 1933 she was broken up at Blyth having been replaced by the *Reina del Pacifico* on the PSNC roster.

QSS Empress of Asia, 1912 (Canadian Pacific)

Gross tonnage:	16,909
Length:	592 feet
Beam:	68.2 feet
Speed:	21.4 Knots (maximum)
Machinery:	Turbines (Fairfield)/quadruple screw
Complement:	284 First Class, 100 Second Class, 808 Asiatic steerage, 475 Crew

There are few finer examples of the Clyde-built ship than the magnificent *Empresses* of the Canadian Pacific Line. Most were built by the Fairfield Shipbuilding and Engineering Company and offered a degree of hitherto unsurpassed luxury for the ocean traveller. Two such vessels were the *Empress of Russia* and her sister *Empress of Asia* both completed in 1912 and destined for the Pacific routes. Each presented a balanced if slightly heavy profile: they were the first large liners to have cruiser sterns. In their white liveries they were an imposing sight although, in the case of the *Asia* , this colour scheme was rejected in favour of a black hull from 1919 till 1926. She was completed in May 1913 having been launched on 23rd November of the previous year and, as CPL's new flagship, departed on her maiden voyage from Liverpool to Hong Kong on 14th June. *Empress of Asia* then sailed for Vancouver to take up service on the Vancouver-Yokohama route. Her time on this was short-lived as she was requisitioned some twelve months later for war service as an armed merchant cruiser. From 2nd August 1914 till 20th March 1916 she performed in this capacity but was thereafter handed back to CPL for further transpacific service. Once again she was called upon for war duty and from 3rd May 1918 till 10th February 1919 she assumed the role of troop transport before being returned to her owners. The ship was extensively overhauled, her passenger capacity revised and her hull painted black. In this condition she resumed service though no longer as the company's flagship, this honour being given to the *Empress of France*. An unusually fast ship for the Pacific the *Empress of Asia* managed on one occasion in July 1924 to make the journey from Yokohama to William Head, British Columbia in 8 days, 14 hours and 48 minutes at an average speed of 20.2 knots proving her to be slightly faster than her sister. Unfortunately her impeccable record was somewhat marred on 11th January 1926 when she collided with the British freighter *Tung Shing* sinking her in the process but luckily with no loss of life; damage to the *Empress* was minimal. On completion of repairs she emerged once more with a white hull and commenced a period of uninterrupted service until 13th February 1941 when war once more called for her to be requisitioned as a troop transport. She sailed from Vancouver that day bound for the UK via the Panama Canal and underwent conversion at Liverpool for her wartime role. On 5th February 1942 while in convoy from Liverpool to Singapore with 2,651 people on board she was sighted by Japanese bombers. In an engagement lasting an hour and a half the ship was attacked by 27 enemy aircraft off the Singapore coast. Five direct hits were scored on her causing the vessel to catch fire. Surprisingly only 19 lives were lost when she finally heeled over and sank some nine miles from Keppel Harbour. She remained on the seabed until 1952 when the International Salvage Association began dismantling the wreck.

TSS Nevasa, 1912 (British India Line)

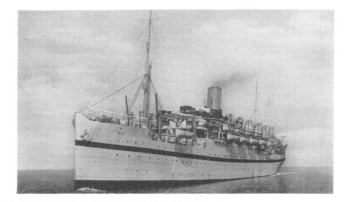

Gross tonnage:	9,071
Length:	480.5 feet
Beam:	58.1 feet
Speed:	14.5 Knots (maximum)
Machinery:	Quadruple expansion engine (Barclay Curle)/twin screw
Complement:	Intended: 128 First Class, 98 Second Class, but requisitioned as a troop transport shortly after completion.

The *Nevasa* was launched on 12th December 1912 from the Barclay, Curle yard on the Upper Clyde and delivered to her owners, the British India Steam Navigation Company, on 5th March the following year. *Nevasa*'s sister ship was the *Neuralia* completed in November 1912 and virtually identical to her younger sister. Like *Nevasa* she was built by Barclay, Curle and became a permanent troopship after short commercial service. While en route to Taranto to embark German POWs she was mined off Southern Italy on 1st May 1945 and sank three and a half hours later. She was not however classed as 'lost in action' as the mine was Italian and Italy was by that time an ally.

Although intended for the UK-Calcutta route, *Nevasa* made only one voyage there before being requisitioned by the Government in August 1914 upon the outbreak of war. *Nevasa* was rapidly converted into a troopship although her role was altered to that of hospital ship with a capacity for 660 beds in January 1915. She served as such until March 1918 during which time she was present at the Salonika and Mesopotamian campaigns and saw service in the East African and Persian Gulf war zones. Twice during 1918 she was chased by enemy submarines but escaped sinking by using her speed and smoke - a fortuitous outcome given that she was employed as a troopship at the time and was filled to capacity.

With the onset of peace *Nevasa* resumed her role with British India on the Calcutta route. She commenced this service in 1919 and completed a total of 14 voyages before being purchased by the Government in August 1925 for conversion into a permanent trooper capable of carrying 1,000 men. The work was undertaken by R H Green & Silley Weir and had the effect of altering her gross tonnage to 9,213. In 1928 she emerged in troopship colours having a white hull with a broad blue band, buff-yellow funnel and green waterline. During the thirties she carried out a series of educational cruises (1935-37) and was present at the Spithead Naval Review (1937) but when war was declared in September 1939 *Nevasa* found herself trooping once more to India and continued to do so over the next two years. In 1943 she took part in the Madagascar campaign then shuttled troops to the Normandy beachheads during the D-Day invasion in June 1944. She then served as Personnel Ship at the Kyaukpyu landings in the Far East before being withdrawn for overhaul in October 1945. This work was completed in London prior to the ship resuming commercial service but by this time *Nevasa* was nearing the end of her 35 year career. She was laid up on the River Blackwater in January 1948, sold to the British Iron and Steel Corporation two months later and finally scrapped at Bo'ness in June of that year.

QSS Calgarian, 1913 (Allan Line)

The *Calgarian* and her half-sister *Alsatian* were the last two large passenger vessels to be built for the famous Allan Line of Glasgow. Although similar in appearance both were products of different yards, Beardmore being responsible for *Alsatian* while her consort was built by Fairfield's in Govan. *Calgarian* was launched on 19th April 1913 and after spending almost a year fitting-out was handed over to her owners on 16th March 1914. Her maiden voyage from Liverpool to St John in Canada took place the following May but her peacetime role was abruptly ended with the outbreak of hostilities in August 1914.

QSS Calgarian

Gross tonnage:	17,521
Length:	590 feet
Beam:	70.2 feet
Speed:	21.6 Knots (maximum)
Machinery:	Turbines (Parsons-Fairfield)/quadruple screw
Complement:	200 First Class, 450 Second Class, 1,000 Third Class, 500 Crew

She was quickly snapped up by the Royal Navy who had her adapted as an armed merchant cruiser in which capacity she entered service with the 10th Cruiser Squadron on 15th September. From July 1917 *Calgarian* ceased to be a unit of the Allan Line whose fortunes had gone rapidly into decline. Her new owners were Canadian Pacific who planned to employ her once again on the North Atlantic after the war. This scheme never came to fruition for on 1st March 1918 she was torpedoed and sunk with the loss of 49 lives by the U-19 west of Rathlin Island, bringing to an end the short career of this stateliest of ships.

TSS Gelria, 1913 (Royal Holland Lloyd)

Gross tonnage:	13,868
Length:	560 feet
Beam:	65.6 feet
Speed:	17.5 Knots (maximum)
Machinery:	Quadruple expansion engines (Stephen)/twin screw
Complement:	250 First Class, 230 Second Class, 140 Third Class, 900 Steerage, 330 Crew

Gelria and her sister *Tubantia* were two graceful ships completed for the Royal Holland Lloyd Line by Alexander Stephen's yard at Linthouse in 1913. *Tubantia* survived less than three years, being torpedoed by the UB-13 near the Noordhinder lightship in March 1916. *Gelria* by comparison completed over thirty years of service before going to the breakers. She was launched on 20th May 1913, completed by the 8th October, and sailed on her maiden voyage from Amsterdam to La Plata on 5th November. This remained her principal route until the *Tubantia* was torpedoed; thereafter she was laid up at Amsterdam until 12th March 1919 when she returned to the South American run once more.

For most of the twenties her career remained unremarkable. In 1921 she was chartered to Rotterdam Lloyd for a voyage to the Dutch East Indies before resuming service to La Plata and, apart from withdrawal for conversion to oil-firing in 1928, here she remained until 5th November 1931 when she was laid-up due to world depression. Two years later she was chartered to the Argentinian Government who planned to use her as an exhibition ship but the scheme failed to materialise. The *Gelria* was again laid-up at Amsterdam on 21st April 1934 before being sold to the Italian Government sixteen months later. She was renamed *Gradisca* and managed by Lloyd Triestino who used the vessel as a troop transport and, on occasion, as a hospital ship during the Abyssinian War. Her role scarcely changed with the onset of World War Two. For the duration she served again as a hospital ship but under German control after 3rd October 1943 and the capitulation of the Italians. While ferrying wounded service men from Salonika to Trieste on 28th October 1944 *Gradisca* was held up by a British submarine and ordered into Alexandria. Over 1,000 troops were disembarked there before the ship was escorted to Algiers. The ship was finally returned to Germany on 20th January 1945 but became a British prize on the conclusion of hostilities. It was while on a voyage from Port Said to Malta on 23rd January 1946 that the *Gradisca* met her fate by running aground off the island of Gavdos. She was salvaged in June of the following year and laid-up at Venice where she languished for another two years before being sold to Soc. Ital. Breda for breaking up. This work was completed by 1950.

TSS Kaisar-i-Hind, 1914 (P& O)

Kaisar-I-Hind was a most handsome vessel and the second ship to bear this unusual name which means 'Emperor of India'. Her predecessor had been built in 1878 and, like the new ship, was the product of Caird and Company of Greenock. She was built for the P & O Line for their London-Bombay mail service and was launched on 27th June 1914. *Kaisar* was the company's most expensive vessel to date costing £363,176, an enormous sum for a ship not destined for the North Atlantic. She was schooner rigged with a straight stem and shapely counter stern. Her two perfectly proportioned and well-raked funnels

81

Gross tonnage:	11,430
Length:	520 feet
Beam:	61.2 feet
Speed:	18.5 Knots (maximum)
Machinery:	Quadruple expansion engines (Caird)/twin screw
Complement:	315 First Class, 333 Second Class

completed the noblest of profiles. Internally she was an improvement on earlier P & O ships; her 1st Class cabins were mainly single berth and each had an electric fan which in southern waters might be regarded as a necessity but which had never been installed in any of the company's vessels before. *Kaisar-i-Hind* set out on her maiden voyage on 1st October 1914 and made a record voyage to Bombay in 17 days and 20 hours and 52 minutes. However, because of the outbreak of war in August 1914 P & O was compelled to run the *Kaisar* on a reduced serivce. The ship's wartime service earned her the nickname 'Lucky Kaisar' for she was attacked on no less than four occasions by U-Boats without coming to grief. In the first three instances all the torpedoes failed to hit their target. Her last encounter with the enemy however, was little short of miraculous. On 22nd April 1918 she was in the Mediterranean with over 3,000 troops and 500 crew members on board when an enemy torpedo struck the ship in the vicinity of her engine room. It failed to explode and only dented her hull plates. Thereafter the damaged plates were painted bright green and remained in this condition until they were replaced some years later. Upon the cessation of hostilities the *Kaisar-i-Hind* continued in Government service repatriating Australian troops and ferrying British troops between Great Britain and India.

In 1920 the ship returned to peacetime service on the route for which she was intended. She was briefly chartered to the Cunard Line the following year and was renamed *Emperor of India*. Cunard had lost many ships during the war and although they had ordered 13 new vessels few of these had been delivered. The company's existing fleet could not cope with the volume of passengers wanting to cross the Atlantic so chartering became a necessity. The *Kaisar* sailed from Southampton for New York on 8th June 1921 and took nine days to complete the crossing. She was almost immediately re-chartered by the American Tourist Agency for a cruise to Scandinavia which proved disastrous for the firm. *Kaisar* had no heating, a necessity in Northern climates, she sailed for much of the time in thick fog and a violent explosion in the stokehold killed three Italian fireman and scalded four engineers forcing her to return to Tilbury on 26th July 1921 one month after the cruise had began. Following an extensive refit *Kaisar* returned to service with P & O on the London—Bombay route and remained on this run virtually for the rest of her career. Even so this was not entirely free of incident. On 22nd May 1930 she lost her port propeller when five days out of Bombay, forcing her to reduce speed to 13.5 knots. She finally arrived in London on 9th June and underwent repair. The following year saw her in the news once more when strong winds caused her to drag her anchor while in Grand Harbour, Malta. This had the effect of causing her to collide with the Italian ship *Citta di Trieste* sinking several wooden lighters in the process. 1929 saw the introduction of the superb *Viceroy of India* on the Bombay route and this enabled P & O to include voyages to the Far East on the *Kaisar*'s schedule. The ship's last voyage was from London to Japan and she departed the capital on 14th January 1938 reaching her destination at the end of the following month. The twenty four year old ship was now well past her best and proving costly to run for, unlike many vessels in that inter-war era, the *Kaisar* had never been converted to oil-firing. P & O reluctantly took the decision to dispose of her and she arrived at Blyth to be broken up by Hughes, Bolkow and Company, the sale price being £28,500.

TSS Naldera, 1917 (P & O Line)

The *Naldera* was Caird and Company's eighty-third vessel and their last before the yard was taken over by Harland and Wolff. She was one of a pair of distinguished three-funnelled liners built for the P & O Line's Australian service. Her sister was the *Narkunda*, a product of the Harland and Wolff yard in Belfast.

Gross tonnage:	16,088
Length:	600 feet
Beam:	62.2 feet
Speed:	17.5 Knots (maximum)
Machinery:	Quadruple expansion engines (Caird)/twin screw
Complement:	426 First Class, 274 Second Class

Work on the *Naldera* began in November 1913 but ceased when war broke out in August 1914. She languished on the Greenock slipway for three years before construction was resumed once more in 1917. The hull was finally launched on 29th December that year with the vessel being fitted out as a troop transport. After the war *Naldera* was returned to P & O and undertook her maiden voyage from London to Sydney on 10th April 1920. Her sister could be easily distinguished by her short raised forecastle - a feature which the Naldera did not have. Both ships were a splendid sight with their three tall, slightly raked funnels and could be regularly seen at Tilbury for much of the inter-war period.

From June 1920 *Naldera* operated the Australia route via Marseilles and Colombo. In July of that year she collided with the Clan Liner *Clan Lamont* which was at anchor in Bombay Harbour and was forced to return to port for repairs although neither ship sustained serious damage. From November 1922 till May 1923 she was on charter to Thomas Cook as the company's cruise ship for their Round the World Tour the fare for which was £1,400, a hugh amount for that time. *Naldera* hit the headlines once more on 2nd October 1924 when the small cargo vessel *Scotstoun Head* collided with her as she was docking at Tilbury causing extensive damage to her port side plates amidships.

In 1927 *Narkunda* was converted to oil-firing but unaccountably *Naldera* remained a coal-burner to the end of her days. The last eight years of her life were not without mishap; while en route to Colombo from Fremantle in July 1930 she encountered violent storms which ripped off several of her ventilators and flooded her number two hold. Four years later, in October 1934, she ran aground in the Suez Canal but was refloated some 24 hours later after much of her cargo had been unloaded to lighten her. One final incident took place on 16th January 1937 when the *Naldera* sustained damage to her starboard propeller whilst docking at Southampton prior to embarking passengers for the Far East.

The ship made two more voyages to Kobe in Japan before ending her 17 year career on 23rd Sptember 1938. P & O then put her up for sale and found a buyer in P & W MacLellan of Glasgow who paid £36,000 for the ship. She left Tilbury for the breaker's yard at Bo'ness on the Firth of Forth on 19th November 1938 thus bringing to an end the eventful career of this splendid ship.

TSS Windsor Castle, 1921 (Union-Castle Line)

Gross tonnage:	18,967
Length:	661 feet
Beam:	72.5 feet
Speed:	18 Knots (maximum)
Machinery:	Geared turbines (Brown)/twin screw
Complement:	235 First Class, 360 Second Class, 275 Third Class, 440 Crew

Although originally earmarked for the Belfast yard of Harland and Wolff, the contract for the *Windsor Castle* was ultimately given to John Brown's at Clydebank as the Irish yard had an already full order book. Seldom can a shipyard have felt such reluctance to undertake an order for the *Windsor Castle* and her Belfast-built sister *Arundel Castle* would already be outdated at the time of their launch. Both were the subject of a torrent of criticism; they were coal-burners at the time when most modern ships used oil and each had a voracious consumption; both steered with some difficulty and, perhaps worst of all, each sported a four-funelled profile which was something of an anachromism by the early twenties. On ships like the White Star's 45,000 ton *Olympic* class these looked magnificently impressive but appeared rather ridiculous on the Union-Castle sisters both of which were under 20,000 tons. In addition this profile was only achieved by taking the uptakes from the boilers through every major public room on each vessel. This alteration attracted much adverse comment and officials at John Brown's tried repeatedly to persuade the Union-Castle Board of Directors to radically change their designs, but without success.

Windsor Castle was launched by Edward, Prince of Wales on 9th March 1921 and entered service on the Southampton-Cape Town route in April of the following year. Despite all the adverse criticism, the ship's accommodation was highly regarded by passengers and crew alike but the design faults were inescapable. These included a type of gantry davit which was supposed to enable the 12 lifeboats postitioned aft of the fourth funnel to be launched inside twenty minutes: in practice the exercise took more than an hour; a two inch gap at the top of the bulkheads of all First Class staterooms was designed to facilitate the circulation of air in warmer climates but equally well could provide a natural draught in the event of fire; harbour pilots too came to loathe the pair because of their inability to respond quickly to telegraphed orders for full astern.

In 1937 *Windsor Castle* was refitted by Harland and Wolff and the ugly duckling was transformed into a stylish, elegant swan. Her forecastle was modernised and lengthened, new turbines were installed and her funnels reduced from four to two, of greater girth. She resumed the South African service once more in January 1938 but was requisitioned for war the next year performing in the role of troop transport. It was while sailing in a convoy 110 nautical miles north-west of Algiers that the *Windsor Castle* was attacked and sunk by German aircraft fortunately without heavy loss of life.

TS Volendam, 1922 (Holland-America Line)

Gross tonnage:	15,434
Length:	472 feet
Beam:	67.3 feet
Speed:	15 Knots (maximum)
Machinery:	Geared Turbines (Brown-Curtis-Harland and Wolff)/ twin screw
Complement:	263 First Class, 436 Second Class, 1,200 Third Class, 350 Crew

On 6th July 1922 the hull of the *Volendam* slid down the ways at the Harland and Wolff yard in Govan and into the Clyde. She and her sister *Veendam*, launched 18th November that year, were the newest additions to the Holland-America Line's fleet and were destined for the North Atlantic. Fitting-out took until 12th October and on 4th November the elegant *Volendam* embarked on her maiden voyage from Rotterdam to New York. This was to remain her regular route until 1940 when she was taken over as a transport by the British Government, but under Cunard management. It was on 30th August that year that she fell victim to a U-boat attack while sailing as a unit of convoy OB 205 from great Britain to New York via Halifax. The *Volendam* was the Convoy Commodore's ship and at the time carried 273 crew and 606 passengers of whom 335 were children. Of these, 15 were travelling with their parents while the remaining 320 were with the Children's Overseas Reception Board (CORB) seeking the safety of Canadian shores. The attack took place some 300 nautical miles off the Irish coast with the U-60 commanded by Oberleutnant Adelbert Schnee initiating the offensive. Two torpedoes struck the ship some 60 feet from the bow although the second of these failed to detonate. Immediately the passengers and crew took to the lifeboats and were picked up shortly after by three other members of the convoy. Despite serious damage the *Volendam* remained afloat and was taken in tow by the salvage tug *Ranger* returning in due course to the UK. The children were later landed at Gourock on the lower Clyde and then ferried home to their anxious parents.

Following extensive repairs the *Volendam* returned to service as a troop transport in July 1941. The ship was handed over to her former owners in July 1945 but was chartered by the British Ministry of Transport from the Holland-America Line for a further year during which time she continued to function as a troopship. Throughout 1946-47 she conveyed members of the allied forces from the Dutch East Indies back to Holland and latterly entered the emigrant service plying the route from Rotterdam to Australia. Towards the end of the forties the *Volendam* returned to her original North Atlantic run operating as a one-class vessel with accommodation for 1,682 passengers. After four years of service between Rotterdam and New York this fine ship was withdrawn from the Holland-America fleet and earmarked for disposal. She was sold to F. Rijsdijk, Hendrik Ido Ambacht, in February 1952 and subsequently broken up.

TSS Franconia, 1922 (Cunard Line)

Gross tonnage:	20,158
Length:	623 feet
Beam:	73.2 feet
Speed:	16 Knots (maximum)
Machinery:	Geared turbines (Brown)/twin screw
Complement:	221 First Class, 356 Second Class, 1,266 Third Class, 414 Crew

The Cunard Line's *Franconia* of 1922 was a most elegant vessel and a product of John Brown's shipyard at Clydebank. She belonged to the *Scythia* Class of intermediate liner built for the company during the early 1920's and was launched on 21st October 1922. On 23rd June the following year she departed Liverpool on her maiden voyage to New York but she was built as a dual-purpose vessel, the intention being to use her extensively for cruising. It was while performing in this role that she ran aground off San Juan, Puerto Rico in 1926, sustaining superficial damage to her hull plates. She finally floated free with the help of the tug *Grebe*. Her passenger accommodation was extended during the ship's winter refit in 1930 and she emerged as a three-class vessel in May of that year. In 1933 *Franconia* was given a white hull in preparation for her world cruise out of New York. A year later she was back in the North Atlantic on the London-New York route, changing to the Liverpool-New York run in 1935. 1936 saw her once more in cruising white, undertaking a world voyage that called at thirty-seven ports and covered a record 41,727 miles.

At the beginning of the war *Franconia* was refitted at Liverpool as a troop transport and shortly set sail for Malta. En route she collided with the Royal Mail Line's *Alcantara* with only minor damage to either ship. In June 1940 she assisted in the evacuation of British forces from northern Norway and again in the evacuation of France during which she was bombed in Quiberon Bay, Brittany but survived to rescue some 8,000 troops and civilians. She took part in the invasion of Sicily on 9th July 1943 and was used as the headquarters ship for the Crimean Yalta conference in which Churchill, Roosevelt and Stalin took part. With the coming of peace *Franconia* was employed in the repatriation of allied troops before being finally paid-off in July 1948. In the course of the war she had carried 149,239 personnel and steamed 319,284 miles. On the 2nd June 1949 *Franconia* entered service on the Canadian run out of Liverpool and just over a year later ran aground once more, this time on Orleans Island, Quebec. She remained there for four days before being refloated and then dry-docked for repairs. Her troubles were not yet over for in April 1954 she experienced engine failure and had to be assisted back to Southampton by another Cunarder *Asia* while 669 of her passengers were transferred to the *Queen Mary*. Escalating repair bills and running costs sealed the fate of this fine ship and after 34 years of service she was scrapped in December 1956 by Thomas W Ward at Inverkeithing.

TSMV Adda, 1922 (Elder Dempster)

Gross tonnage:	7816
Length:	435.3 feet
Beam:	57.3 feet
Speed	14 Knots (maximum)
Machinery:	4 stroke single acting diesel (H & W/Burmeister and Wain)/ twin screw
Complement:	360 passengers

The *Adda* was completed by Harland and Wolff Limited at Greenock for the African Steamship Company in November 1922 and was the second motorship to be managed by the Elder Dempster group, the first being the *Aba* of 1918 which was acquired by them for the British and African Steam Navigation Company in 1920. She was a most handsome vessel having an elegant counter stern, the fashion for which had all but passed, and a well-proportioned tall funnel. The vogue for squat stacks on motorships appeared at the end of the decade and fortunately *Adda* was spared this indignity. (As a concession to modernity these did little to enhance the appearance of any ship, giving them a kind of sawn-off, chunky look.) Her graceful superstructure, indicative of a passenger carrying vessel, belied the fact that she was essentially a working cargo-liner which for most of her career plied the same route to the African continent. *Adda* underwent a transfer of ownership on 15th August 1932 being wholly taken over by Elder Dempster Lines Limited. She continued to enjoy a trouble-free if uneventful career until 8th June 1941 when she was torpedoed by a German submarine off Monrovia with a loss of 12 lives.

TSS Hector, 1924 (Blue Funnel Line)

Gross tonnage:	11,198
Length:	530 feet
Beam:	62.3 feet
Speed:	15.5 Knots (maximum)
Machinery:	Geared turbines (Scott's)/twin screw
Complement:	175 First Class, 80 Crew

The *Hector* was one of four passenger-cargo liners built for the Blue Funnel Line during the mid nineteen-20's, the others being *Sarpedon, Antenor* and *Patroclus*. They were aristocatic-looking ships bearing the instantly recognisable profile long associated with their owner, the tall vertical pale blue funnel with deep black top, together with names culled from Classical Greek mythology. *Hector* differed from her sisters only insofar as she sported three lifeboats instead of two on her boat deck and had no boat on the bridge deck derrick house. In all other respects she was identical. She was launched from the yard of Scott's Shipbuilding and Engineering Company, Greenock on 18th June 1924 and entered service on the Liverpool—Far East route on 24th September that year. Her years of service until the Second World War were uneventful but in 1940 she was requisitioned by the navy for duties as an armed merchant cruiser, a role she efficiently performed until 5th April 1942 when she fell victim to Japanese bombers during an air raid on Colombo Harbour. This year was the worst in the company's history for war losses, with a total of eighteen ships being despatched to the bottom by both the Germans and the Japanese. By the end of the conflict Blue Funnel had seen 41 of their ships destroyed totalling 321,673 gross tons with a loss of 324 lives. In 1946 the submerged wreck of the *Hector* was refloated and beached, whereupon she was broken up where she lay.

SS Britannia, 1926 (Anchor Line)

Gross tonnage:	8,799
Length:	460 feet
Beam:	59 feet
Speed:	13 Knots (maximum)
Machinery:	Quadruple expansion engine (Stephen)/single screw
Complement:	175 First Class

Britannia was launched during the early months of 1926 and was destined to operate on the Anchor Line's Glasgow-Bombay service for her entire career. She was built at the Alexander Stephen's yard at Linthouse in Glasgow and was essentially a cargo-liner with passenger carrying facilities for 175 people. Her maiden voyage was undertaken in March 1926 and she regularly plied to the Indian subcontinent over the next two years but she proved to be an expensive ship to operate. In 1928 the directors of the Anchor Line agreed to have her quadruple expansion engines replaced by the more economical Bauer-Wauch exhaust turbine which had the effect of reducing her fuel bills by some 20%. When war came in 1939 *Britannia* remained on her regular Bombay route and it was while sailing to India on 25th March 1941 that she came to grief. Some 750 miles west of Freetown (Sierra Leone) she encountered the German auxiliary cruiser *Thor* known as *Raider E* to the British authorities. *Thor* sported six x 5.9" guns plus torpedo tubes and after an hour-long engagement had reduced the *Britannia* to little more than a hulk. Of the 484 passengers and crew aboard her, 249 survived following the order to abandon ship. 63 of these were picked up from one lifeboat by the Spanish steamer *Bachi*, while a further 38 reached Brazil after a journey of some 23 days which required great fortitude in the face of appalling hardship. The *Thor* herself was destroyed on 30th November 1942 when the supply tanker *Uckermark*, formerly the prison ship *Altmark*, exploded and sank in the harbour at Yokohama, Japan.

TSMV Viceroy of India, 1928 (P & O)

Viceroy of India was the first European owned turbo-electric vessel. She was a product of the Alexander Stephen yard and was built for the P & O company in the late twenties. Originally it had been the intention to name her *Taj Mahal* but this idea was dropped only days before launch. The *Viceroy* was sumptuously furnished in period style; her First Class Lounge decorated in 18th century fashion, dining saloon in French style of the same era while her principal smoking room was completed in an old baronial style and included a collection of some of the effects of Bonnie Prince Charlie. There was also an indoor Pompeiian swimming pool.

The ship was launched on 15th September 1928 by the wife of the Viceroy of India and undertook her trials between 18th February and 6th March 1929. She made her maiden voyage for P & O on 29th March departing London bound for Bombay via Marseilles, Malta and Suez and arrived at her destination on 26th April. Thereafter she returned to Tilbury and spent the summer months cruising out of London. On her return to the Indian service she broke the London-Bombay speed record with a time of 16 days, 1 hour and 42 minutes. In the early hours of 5th September 1935 the *Viceroy* was involved in the dramatic rescue of passengers from the Cunard—White Star Liner *Doric* which had been in collision with a French coaster *Formigny* some miles off the Portuguese coast. The ship was some 40 miles from the scene of the accident and raced to the rescue. Shortly after, the Orient Line's *Orion* arrived to offer further assistance. The *Viceroy* transferred 241 passengers from the *Doric* with the *Orion* saving the remainder. Apart from sustaining minor damage to her rudder after grounding in the Suez Canal in April 1937, the vessel's career passed without incident until the war. Once more cruising formed part of her schedule and included voyages to the Atlantic Isles and the northern capitals in the months prior to hosilities breaking out. She took over the route to India and Shanghai which had been intended for the *Rawalpindi*. The latter had fought a gallant action on 23rd November 1939 with the German battlecruisers *Scharnhorst* and *Gneisenau* and in an exchange lasting 40 minutes the *Rawalpindi*, hopelessly out-gunned,

TSMV Viceroy of India

Gross tonnage:	19,648
Length:	612 feet
Beam:	76.2 feet
Speed:	19 Knots (maximum)
Machinery:	Turbo-electric/twin screw
Complement:	415 First Class, 258 Second Class, 417 Crew

finally slid beneath the waves taking with her 265 of her crew. The *Viceroy* made a further three voyages to the Far East before being sent to the Clyde for partial refit as a troop transport in November 1940. This conversion work was completed in Liverpool during February and March the following year and for the next 18 months she was engaged in full-time trooping duties to Port Said (via the Cape) and Bombay.

The *Viceroy* sailed from the Clyde on 26th October 1942 as part of the *Operation Torch* convoy to Algiers. She arrived safely on 7th November, disembarked troops and left for home three days later. In the early hours of the 11th she unexpectedly came upon the U-407 charging her batteries on the surface and was promptly torpedoed. Her engine room exploded killing two engineers and two firemen. In a sinking condition she was abandoned by her passengers and crew - a total of 450 souls. All were picked up by *HMS Boadicea* and taken to Gibraltar for repatriation aboard the Union-Castle Liner *Llangibby Castle*. After staying afloat for just under four hours the *Viceroy of India* finally sank by the stern in a position some 31 miles north of Oran bringing to an end the career of this truly fine ship.

SS Comedian, 1929 (Thos and Jas Harrison)

Gross tonnage:	5,122
Length:	395.5 feet
Beam:	52.5 feet
Speed:	11.5 Knots (maximum)
Machinery:	Triple expansion engine (Connell)/single screw
Complement:	40 crew (approx)

The *Comedian* was one of a class of ten cargo vessels built in the late twenties for the Harrison Line by the yards of Charles Connell, D & W Henderson and Cammell, Laird of Birkenhead. Connell completed five ships (*Planter, Rancher, Custodian, Observer* and *Comedian*), Henderson was responsible for another (*Designer*) while the English yard built the remaining four (*Logician, Tactician, Recorder* and *Contractor*). All sported the Harrison trademark having the 'trades and professions' style of nomenclature. They were noteworthy vessels insofar as they were the final version of the traditional deck boats with a single poop lifeboat on the port side only. In appearance they were not dissimilar to members of the Harrison fleet of thirty years earlier.

Although lacking the glamour of the North Atlantic passenger vessels these sturdy ships performed efficiently on the South African routes for which they were intended and could carry sufficient coal for the round trip. The *Comedian* was the odd one out of the class being slightly smaller than her sisters. She was launched on 20th August 1929 from the Connell yard and completed her fitting out by October that year. Her subsequent career was undramatic with the exception of a collision with Chapman and Willan's *Koranton* off Halifax, Nova Scotia in February 1940. Such was the extent of the damage to her hull that repairs took some four months to complete. Her days plying the South African trade routes ended in October 1950 when she was sold to the India National Steamship Company and was renamed *Indian Importer*. She sailed under their colours for about six years before being acquired by Wheelock, Mardan and Company of Hong Kong for the sum of £210,000 and was given yet another name, *South Birch*, in the process. By now the ship was approaching thirty years of strenuous service and maintenance costs were beginning to escalate so the decision was taken to withdraw her prior to laying up. In July 1959 she was sold for scrap to a Hong Kong breaker. Her two remaining sisters, *Tactician* and *Recorder* followed her shortly afterwards. Although never headliners it was ships like these which formed the backbone of Britain's maritime supremacy.

TSS Llangibby Castle, 1929 (Union-Castle Line)

Gross tonnage:	11,951
Length:	507 feet
Beam:	66.3 feet
Speed:	14.5 Knots (maximum)
Machinery:	Diesel by Burmeister and Wain (H & W)/twin screw
Complement:	250 First Class, 200 Third Class

The *Llangibby Castle* was the first of the Union-Castle Line's four motorships produced between 1929 and 1931, the others being the *Dunbar Castle* (1930), *Winchester Castle* (1930) and *Warwick Castle* (1931). She was built by the Harland and Wolff yard in Govan and was launched on 4th July 1929. After fitting out she undertook her speed trials on 21st November following which she was formally handed over to her owners. She left London on her maiden voyage round Africa on 5th December and plied the same route for the next ten years. Shortly after war was declared, the *Llangibby Castle* was requisitioned by the Admiralty and converted to a troop tranport. In this role she had an eventful career. While berthed at Liverpool on the night of 21/22 December 1940 she fell victim to enemy bombers although the damage inflicted was superficial. Over a year later, on 16th January 1942, while crossing the Atlantic with over 1,400 troops on board, she was torpedoed by the U-402 and lost her stern gun and rudder but was able to reach Horta under her own power. Three months later she arrived back in Britain, was repaired and equipped as an Infantry Ship, and before long was again in action. At Oran where an eight inch enemy shell struck her engineer's accommodation on the boat deck while she was landing troops in November 1942. She

TSMV Derbyshire

Gross tonnage: 11,650
Length: 502 feet
Beam: 66.3 feet
Speed: 15 Knots (maximum)
Machinery: Sulzer diesel (Fairfield)/twin screw
Complement: 291 First Class, 224 Crew

98

returned fire and destroyed the battery using her six inch gun. Towards the end of this action she accidentally collided with the Dutch ship *Tegelberg* and sustained serious damage. Her complement of troops was transferred to the *Llanstephan Castle* for onward passage to Algiers.

In December 1946 she was returned to her owners who sent her back to Govan for an extensive refit and on completion she returned to the London—round Africa service once more. The *Llangibby Castle* remained operative for a further eight years and completed her last voyage for Union-Castle on 18th June 1954. Eleven days later she departed Tilbury for the last time having been sold for demolition to John Cashmore Limited of Newport, Monmouthsire.

TSMV Derbyshire, 1935 (Bibby Line)

From its inception the Bibby Line established a reputation as owners of a fine fleet of distinctive vessels. With the coming of the age of steam the company adopted a profile which was to remain relatively unchanged until the onset of World War Two. Units of the fleet boasted no less than four tall pole masts which were fashionable during the 1880's and 90's throughout the mercantile marine generally but by the 1930's was distinctly dated. By this time however, it had become the Bibby trademark and was recognised worldwide.

Among the last of the fleet to adhere to this tradition was the cargo liner *Derbyshire*, a product of the Fairfield Shipbuilding and Engineering Company, which was launched on 14th June 1935 and made her maiden voyage from Liverpool to Rangoon in early November. In 1939, following the outbreak of war, she was requisitioned as an armed merchant troop cruiser and performed in this role until February 1942 when she was converted to a troop transport. The next year saw her being used as a landing ship but she reverted to her trooping duties that autumn and carried these out until October 1946 when she was finally released from naval service and handed back to her owners. The *Derbyshire* then underwent extensive refitting and modernisation during which her masts were reduced to two and her tonnage reclassified to 10,641 gross. In 1948 she resumed service on the Liverpool—Rangoon route and remained there for the next fifteen years before being sold to a Hong Kong breaker. The *Derbyshire* arrived there on the 18th February 1964 bringing to an end nearly thirty years of active service.

TSS Canton, 1938 (P & O Line)

Gross tonnage:	15,784
Length:	563 feet
Beam:	73.2 feet
Speed:	20 Knots (maximum)
Machinery:	Geared turbines (Stephen)/twin screw
Complement:	260 First Class, 220 Second Class, 370 Crew

A product of Alexander Stephen and Sons of Linthouse, the *Canton* was launched on 14th April 1938 and handed over to her owners, P & O, on 9th September that year. She was the last of the company's ships to appear in the traditional black livery which was for so long a feature of P & O liners and the last vessel to be built for the line by Stephen's. Her intended route was to China and Japan and it was to Hong Kong that the *Canton* embarked on her maiden voyage on 7th October. It was an eventful year for the ship; in March she collided with the French liner *Marechal Joffre* while entering Hong Kong harbour in dense fog and suffered a gaping hole in her starboard side near her engine room which put her out of action for three weeks; two months later, on 10th May 1939 she was in the news once more when she rescued 35 passengers from the small Danish liner *Alsia* on fire off the coast of Ceylon. On 26th August 1939 she was requisitioned by the Admiralty for conversion to an armed merchant cruiser and, armed with eight 6" and two 3" guns, she commenced her war service on the North Atlantic Patrol in November. While at sea early in January 1940 the *Canton*'s master was informed by the Admiralty that his ship should return to Greenock prior to being transferred to patrol duty off the east coast of South America. The ship encountered appalling weather on the journey back to the Clyde and ran aground on the rocks off Barra Head, severely damaging her hull and flooding two of her forward holds. Her crew prepared to abandon ship but early on the morning of the 11th she finally pulled herself clear and with the destroyer *Impulsive* and the *AMC California* standing by she set a course for the Clyde and arrived there two days later. She was beached in the Holy Loch and after temporary repairs, limped back to Prince's Dock in Glasgow and an extensive refit by Barclay, Curle and Company.

Her days were nothing if not eventful; she narrowly missed being torpedeod by a U-Boat off the west coast of Ireland while on convoy escort duty in June 1940; the following February she nearly sank the British submarine *HMS Thunderbolt* which she mistook for the enemy and which in turn mistook her for a German merchant ship; in the Atlantic in July 1941 she intercepted the enemy cargo vessel *Karnak* which was disguised as a Dutch freighter and whose crew promptly scuttled her when the *Canton* opened fire having received no response to her order to stop. She rescued survivors from the German raider *Atlantis* after she was sunk by *HMS Devonshire* in the Atlantic at the end of November 1941. By this time the *Canton* boasted quite a formidable armament for a merchant cruiser having nine 6" guns, two twin 4" guns, two 2 pounder pom-poms and 16 Oerlikons but she underwent a change of role in March 1944 when she was sent to Port Suez for conversion to a troop transport. She remained as such until the end of the war by which time she had sailed 278,797 miles as an Admiralty vessel.

In 1947 the *Canton* was returned to her builders for refitting as a passenger liner and emerged for her trials on 28th September sporting a new colour scheme of white hull and superstructure crowned by a buff funnel. On 17th October she sailed from Tilbury bound for Hong Kong and the start of twelve years of service on the route for which she had been intended. *Canton* was a popular and successful ship and a firm favourite with travellers to the Far East, but by the early sixties she was well past her best. Her engines required constant care and maintenance and, unlike her modern counterparts, she lacked air-conditioning, a facility which post-War travellers had come to expect. P & O decided to withdraw the 24 year old ship from service and on 31st August she set sail on her final voyage from London to Hong Kong where she was broken up by the Leung Yau Shipbreaking Company.

MV Corinaldo, 1949 (Donaldson Line)

Gross tonnage:	8,392
Length:	474.5 feet
Beam:	63.3 feet
Speed:	15.5 Knots (maximum)
Machinery:	Diesels (Doxford type by Barclay, Curle and Company)
Complement:	12 passengers-one class

This handsome vessel was ordered by the Donaldson Line for their South American service and launched from the yard of Charles Connell and Company early in 1949. *Corinaldo* was essentially a cargo vessel but with limited accommodation for 12 passengers. She had 4 decks and had 48 compartments air conditioned for carrying fruit. A further 6 holds were available for the trans-shipment of general-purpose cargo.

On 12th March 1949 she made her maiden voyage on the Glasgow-River Plate service and continued on this route until 1952 when she was transferred to the North Pacific run ferrying general cargo to Panama then bananas for the rest of the voyage before returning homeward with a cargo of apples. In 1958 *Corinaldo* returned to the South American service one hundred years after the company's founders had inaugurated it and continued to operate there for the next 9 years. In 1967 the Chairman of the company, F A Donaldson recommended that four of the Line's ships be sold leaving only the *Letitia* to fly the Donaldson colours. *Corinaldo* was purchased by the China Navigation Company for further trading and was renamed *Ningpo*. Almost immediately she was resold to Criomar Incorporated of Monrovia who christened her *Kinaros* before placing her in service once more as a general purpose-carrier. Her career finally came to an end in 1979 when she was laid-up prior to scrapping. Donaldson's decision to sell *Corinaldo* was also the beginning of the end for the firm. Within months the Board of Directors, with the agreement of the majority shareholders, opted for voluntary liquidation of the group bringing to an end 112 years of service.

TSMV Rangitane, 1949 (New Zealand Line)

Gross tonnage:	21,867
Length:	609 feet
Beam:	78.1 feet
Speed:	17 Knots (maximum)
Machinery:	Diesels (Doxford type by John Brown)/twin screw
Complement:	416 passengers-one class

When the board of the New Zealand Line took the decision to order new tonnage for their fleet in the late 1940's, it was with the Vickers-Armstrong and John Brown yards that the contracts were placed. The Newcastle firm completed the *Rangitoto* in August 1949 while her Clyde-built sister *Rangitane* appeared in December that same year having been launched on 30th June. She set out on her maiden voyage from London to Wellington on 27th January 1950 and continued to serve this route until 1968. A year earlier she was acquired by new owners, the Federal Steam Navigation Company, without any deviation from her usual schedule. However, she flew their house flag for less than a year before being sold to Astroguardo Cia Nav of Piraeus. A change of name accompanied this change of ownership, the vessel now being called *Jan*. She made one voyage to Formosa (now Taiwan)

TSS Uganda

Gross tonnage:	14,434
Length:	539.8 feet
Beam:	71.3 feet
Speed:	18 Knots (maximum)
Machinery:	Geared turbines (Parsons)/twin screw
Complement:	167 First Class, 133 Tourist Class

under this name before being despatched to Kaohsiung to be broken up. Fortunately the shipping magnate C.Y. Tung stepped in and purchased her with the intention of using her exclusively for cruising. She was renamed *Oriental Esmeralda* and registered for Oriental Latin American Lines Incorporated, Monrovia. Following a refit at Hong Kong in January 1969 she departed for round-the-world service on 4th June cruising out of San Diego, California.

TSS Uganda, 1952 (British India)

Although originally to be called *Karatina* , the ship which left the ways of the Barclay, Curle shipyard on 15th January 1952 bore the name *Uganda*. She and her sister, *Kenya* were handsome vessels and virtually identical except for the fact that *Uganda*'s funnel was some 12 feet taller than her consort's. *Uganda*'s maiden voyage to Durban took place in August that year, but the following month saw her temporarily out of action when she damaged her port propeller at Dar-es-Salam. Her subsequent career was routine until 1967 except for a change of colour scheme in 1955 when she appeared in cuising white. With the closure of the Suez Canal in 1967 her regular service was ended. She arrived in London on 14th January and two months later left for Hamburg for conversion into an educational cruise ship. When this work was completed in February 1968 *Uganda*'s gross tonnage had altered to 16,907 with capacity for 304 Cabin Class and 920 Students. The ship had 43 dormitories, 14 classrooms, a library, 400 seat assembly hall which doubled as a cinema, two swimming pools and, for the first time, comprehensive air-conditioning. *Uganda* undertook her first student cruise from Southampton on 27th February and continued to operate these services until the early eighties. In 1972 she became a vessel of the P & O passenger fleet although she retained her old British India colours. Six years later she carried a record number of passengers and was operating well into the black making 1978 her best year ever.

Uganda's finest hour came during April 1982 following the Argentinian invasion of the Falkland Islands when she was requisitioned at Alexandria in Egypt for conversion into a hospital ship. This work began on 16th April and when completed the ship had been given a helicopter deck aft, refuelling-at-sea gantry equipment, and her interiors converted into wards. All these conversions were completed in 65 hours. She carried a staff of 12 doctors and 124 other medical personnel. The British forces nicknamed her 'Mother Hen' while her

'Chicks' were the hydrographic vessels *Hecla, Heraldu* and *Hydra* which ferried the wounded to *Uganda*. Three days after British forces landed on the Falklands she was buzzed by two Argentinian planes but not attacked and in less than a week *Uganda* was operating close inshore acting as coordinator for all hospital ships including three Argentinian vessels to whom were transferred 150 casualties.

With the surrender of the Argentinian forces in June 1982 she was relieved of her duties. Her huge red crosses, which had been painted on her hull, were removed and her funnel was painted buff yellow. *Uganda* left for Southampton with a full complement of troops on 18th July and arrived back in the UK on 9th August after completing 113 days of service. She resumed her peacetime role as a student cruise ship in September but was withdrawn from service on 16th January 1983, whereupon the Ministry of Defence chartered her for use as a troop transport between Ascension Island and Port Stanley. In 1984 this was extended for a further year until April 1985. On 25th *Uganda* arrived at Falmouth and was promptly laid up in the Fal. She was placed on the disposal list in March the following year and, despite vigorous efforts to preserve her as a floating monument to the age of the great liners, she was sold to the Triton Shipping Company of London. Bearing the name *Triton* and with Jamaican registry, she embarked on her final voyage to Kaohsiung on 20th May 1986 and while awaiting a breakers berth, was blown ashore, coming to rest on her side. She remains there to this day.

TSS Empress of Britain, 1955 (Canadian Pacific)

The *Empress of Britain* together with her sisters *Empress of England* and the slightly larger *Empress of Canada* made their appearance in response to the challenge presented to CPL by the four vessels of Cunard's *Saxonia* Class. Almost as soon as *Saxonia* left the ways at John Brown's yard, the order for the first of the new *Empresses* was placed with Fairfield of Glasgow. *Empress of Britain* was launched by Queen Elizabeth II on 22nd June 1955, undertook her trials on 9th and 10th March the following year and on the 20th April sailed on her maiden voyage from Liverpool to Montreal. She was in fact a dual-purpose ship operating on the North Atlantic between Liverpool, Greenock, Quebec City and Montreal while undertaking cruising duties to the tropics during the winter months, usually out of New York.

106

When she first made her appearance the world's maritime press hailed her as a triumph: *care has been taken in her design to provide everything possible for passengers' comfort in the best traditions of ocean travel* (Syren and Shipping). The *Empress* was a graceful ship projecting a well-balanced silhouette with just the right degree of streamlining yet her service with Canadian Pacific was remarkably brief. With the advent of the *Empress of Canada* which took over the New York-Caribbean cruise trade, the remaining two sisters were chartered in the winter season usually to the Travel Savings Association, an arrangement which proved lucrative over several years. When this work was no longer available one of the twins had to be declared surplus to requirements and it was the *Empress of Britain* which was selected for disposal. She was sold to the Transoceanic Navigation Compamy, a subsidiary of the Greek Line, for service between the Mediterranean ports and North Africa. The handing over ceremony took place on 16th November 1964 and two days later she was re-christened *Queen Anna Maria* before being sent to Genoa for an extensive refit. Her stern was rebuilt as a lido area incorporating no less than five swimming pools; private bathrooms were installed in every cabin and the ship made fully air-conditioned. *Queen Anna Maria* operated in the Mediterranean in concert with the Greek Line's *Olympia*, herself a product of the Clyde yard of Alexander Stephen. Her itinerary included Haifa, Limassol, Piraeus, Messina, Naples, Lisbon, the Azores, Halifax and New York while in winter she cruised to the Caribbean and undertook eight-week cruises to the Mediterranean and the Black Sea. The only hiccup in what was a remarkably smooth period of service came on 19th February 1967 when the *Queen Anna Maria* ran aground off Kingston, Jamaica and remained stranded there for just over a week.

The 1970's proved to be an unhappy time for the Greek Line. The company was in serious financial difficulty and the crisis reached a head in early 1975 when it was revealed that creditors intended to have the Greek Line's flagship impounded at New York. On 11th January the *Queen Anna Maria* sailed down the St Lawrence without passengers in the early hours of dawn to escape the bankers' grasp and arrived at Piraeus on the 22nd. She was laid-up at Perama until December before being purchased at auction by Carnival Cruise Lines of Miami, who by now also owned the *Empress of Canada* (operating under the name *Mardi Gras*). The ship was renamed *Carnivale* and at the time of writing is still cruising in the Caribbean.

TSS Empress of Britain

Gross tonnage:	25,516
Length:	640 feet
Beam:	85.3 feet
Speed:	21 Knots (maximum)
Machinery:	Geared turbines (Brown)/twin screw
Complement:	160 First Class, 894 Tourist Class, 464 Crew

TSMV Kungsholm, 1965 (Swedish-America Line)

There have been four vessels named *Kungsholm* this century; the first in 1901, the second in 1928, the third in 1953 and the most recent in 1965. All were first class ships, particulary the *Kungsholm* of 1953 which was one of the finest liners of the post-war era and a product of the De Schelde Shipyards of Flushing, Holland. Swedish ships have long been noted for their impeccably high standards and degree of sophistication and it was with its constant emphasis on such factors that the Swedish-America Line determined to order a replacement for this vessel after only 12 years in service. The new *Kungsholm* was launched from the John Brown shipyard at Clydebank on 14th April 1965 and was at once recognised as an updated version of the older ship. As in the earlier vessel her forward mast was placed above the bridge; she had a sharply raked, flared bow and, in her Swedish-America Line colours of white and yellow, she looked every inch a flagship. Her two funnels sported the company's logo - blue discs encircling three golden crowns. At night when floodlit she was a truly magnificent sight.

Kungsholm undertook her trials on 19th November 1965 and was delivered to her owners on 17th March the following year. Her maiden voyage from Gothenburg to New York commenced a month later on 22nd April and thereafter she was mainly used for cruising. However, like her predecessor, her career with Swedish-America was short-lived for she was sold to Flagship Cruises, Monrovia in August 1975. *Kungsholm* was officially handed over to her new owners on 6th October and subsequently undertook extensive cruising out of New York. This service was also short-lived for in June 1978 P & O acquired the ship for their Australian cruise programme. She underwent extensive refitting which included the construction of a further 86 cabins and an additional swimming pool. Externally there were changes too. Her forward funnel was removed and the remaining one heightened while her main mast also disappeared. None of these changes enhanced her appearance in the least. In order to bring her into line with her new consorts *Island Princess* and *Pacific Princess* a change of name was required and so the *Kungsholm* made her debut with P & O as the *Sea Princess*.

Her cruising schedule took her to Hobart, Singapore, Hong Kong, Manila, Jakarta, Bali, Rabaul and the Pacific Islands but she was not altogether a success on this route. The company took the decision to

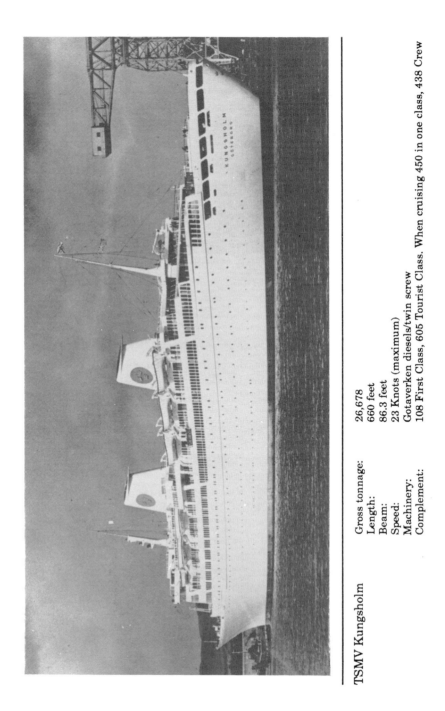

TSMV Kungsholm

Gross tonnage:	26,678
Length:	660 feet
Beam:	86.3 feet
Speed:	23 Knots (maximum)
Machinery:	Gotaverken diesels/twin screw
Complement:	108 First Class, 605 Tourist Class. When cruising 450 in one class, 438 Crew

transfer her to Southampton and replace her with the *Oriana*. She arrived there on 21st April 1982 and underwent a brief refit at the Vospers yard which included the fitting of bow-thrusters. There was some delay before she finally embarked on a cruise to the eastern Mediterranean for by this time the Falklands conflict had begun. *Canberra* was already in the South Atlantic and the Government were undecided whether or not to use the *Sea Princess* as a troopship. On 27th May the word came through that the ship would would not be requisitioned for war duties and the next day she sailed for the Mediterranean. Since then her career has blossomed in the cruise market. In January 1983 she undertook a 90 day world cruise and visited Shanghai two years later, some 44 years after the last P & O ship had done so. Although no longer the sleek beauty of her youth *Sea Princess* survives as an active member of the P & O cruising fleet.

Appendix

Principal Clyde Shipbuilders in the 19th Century

Ailsa Shipbuilding Company	Troon	1885-
Aitken & Mansel	Kelvinhaugh/Whiteinch	1863-1889
Anderson & Gilmore	Glasgow	1841-1847
Anderson & Lyall	Govan, Glasgow	1880's
Barclay	Cartsdyke, Greenock	1860's
Ardrossan Shipbuilding Co	Ardrossan	1873-1899
Ayr Shipbuilding Co	Ayr	1870's
John Barclay	Stobcross, Glasgow	1818-1844
Peter Barclay & Sons	Ardrossan	1860's
Robert Barclay & Co	Stobcross	1844-1845
Robert Barclay & Curle	Stobcross	1845-1863
Barclay, Curle and Co	Stobcross	1863-1874
Barclay, Curle and Co	Whiteinch, Glasgow	1855-
Barclay Robertson & Co	Ardrossan	1870's
J Barnhill	Cartsdyke	1844-1847
John Barr	Kelvinhaugh, Glasgow	1850's
Barr & MacNab	Abercorn, Paisley, West Renfrew	1838-1847
Barr & Shearer	Ardrossan	1844-1873
Birrell, Stenhouse & Co	Dumbarton	1874-1889
Robert Black	Kelvinhaugh	1840-1851
Blackwood and Gordon	Paisely/Port Glasgow	1846-1900
John Bourne & Co	Greenock	1853-1855
William Burrell & Son	Hamiltonhill,Glasgow	1875-1903
Burrell & Son	Dumbarton	1881-1884
Caird & Co	Cartsdyke/Westburn Greenock	1840-1922
Campbell & Co	Paisley	1880-1881
Campbeltown Shipbuilding Co	Campbeltown	1877-1922
Carmichael, MacLean & Co	Greenock	1895-1898
R & A Carswell	Greenock	1816-1832
Chalmers, Scott & McKivett	Govan	1896-1899
W Chalmers and Co Ltd	Rutherglen	1903-1920
R Chambers & Co	Dumbarton	1877-1881
Chambers Brothers	Dumbarton	1896-1900
Clyde Shipbuilding Co	Greenock	1864-1966
Clydebank Engineering and Shipbuilding Company Ltd	Clydebank	1897-1899

Charles Connell & Co Ltd	Scotstoun, Glasgow	1861-1968
Cornwallis	Greenock	1820-1821
J Crawford	Dumbarton	1884
Culzean Steam Launch & Yacht Works	Culzean	1880-1887
D M Cumming Ltd	Blackhill, Glasgow	1880's-1920's
W S Cumming	Blackhill, Glasgow	c1882
Cunliffe and Dunlop	Port Glasgow	1869-1881
Alexander Denny and Brother	Dumbarton	1849-1859
Archibald Denny	Dumbarton	1853-1866
William Denny & Son	Dumbarton	1818-1833
William Denny & Brothers	Dumbarton	1844-1963
Denny & McLean	Dumbarton	1853-1866
Denny & Rankin	Dumbarton	1838-1865
Dobie & Co	Govan	1866-1884
Dobie, Hedderwick and McGaw	Govan	1864-1866
Donald and MacFarlane	Cartvale. Paisley	1867-1868
Robert Duncan & Co	Greenock	1830-1841
Robert Duncan & Co	Port Glasgow	1862-1934
David J Dunlop and Co	Port Glasgow	1881-1911
John Elder & Co	Fairfield. Govan	1870-1886
Fairfield Shipbuilding and Engineering Company Limited	Govan	1886-1965
William Fife and Son	Fairlie	1812-1930's
Fleming and Ferguson	Paisley	1885-1969
John Fullarton and Co	Paisley	1866-1928
Hall, Brown, Butterly and Co	Govan	1892-1912
William Hamilton and Co	Port Glasgow	1871-1963
Hanna, Donald (& Wilson)	Paisley	1851-1895
J & J Hay	Kirkintilloch	1868-1958
D & W Henderson	Meadowside, Glasgow	1873-1962
J Henderson and Son	Renfrew	1847-1861
Henderson, Coulborn and Co	Renfrew	1861-1874
Henderson, Spence and Co	Dumbarton	1866-1870
Laurence Hill and Co	Port Glasgow	1856-1869
J W Hoby and Co	Renfrew	1850-1860
J Howden and Co Ltd	Glasgow	1862-
Hutson and Corbet Ltd	Kelvinhaugh	1875-1950's
A & J Inglis Ltd	Anderston/Pointhouse	1847-1962
Irvine Shipbuilding and Engineering Co	Irvine	1898-1912
W Jackson and Co	Port Dundas, Glasgow	1850's-1890's
William Johnston	Greenock	1836-1841
Kirkpatrick, McIntyre and Co	Cartside, Greenock	1863-1867

James Lamont and Co Ltd	Greenock/Port Glasgow	1870-1979
James Lang	Dumbarton	1815-1822
Lang and Denny	Dumbarton	1822-1839
J G Lawrie	Whiteinch, Glasgow	1854-1875
Lobnitz and Co Ltd	Renfrew	1895-1957
Lobnitz, Coulborn and Co	West Renfrew	1874-1895
London & Glasgow Engineering & Iron Shipbuilding Company Ltd	Govan	1864-1912
Lyon and Foster	Greenock	1869-1871
John McAllister	Dumbarton	1820's-1838
J McArthur and Co	Paisley	1882-1900
MacArthur and Alexander	Govan	1839-1841
John McAuslan	Dumbarton	1839-1851
Charles McBride	Greenock	1871-1877
McCulloch and Paterson	Port Glasgow	1869-1871
McFadyen	Port Glasgow	1872-1874
A McFarlane	Dumbarton	1831-1844
T McGill	Bowling	1825-1851
McGill and Gilmour	Irvine	1887-1895
P MacGregor and Sons	Kirkintilloch	1887-1921
H McIntyre and Co	Paisley	1877-1885
McKellar and McMillan	Dumbarton	1872-1876
McKirdy	Greenock	1820-1840
S McKnight and Co Ltd	Ayr	1884-1902
Archibald MacLachlan	Dumbarton	1812-1818
Robert McLea	Rothesay	1853-1872
Hugh McLean and Sons Ltd	Govan	1880-1943
Archibald McMillan and Son	Dumbarton	1834-1930
James McMillan	Greenock	1850's-1860's
McMillan and McDonald	Greenock	1865-1867
McNab and Co	Greenock	1863-1872
Mackie and Thomson	Govan	1888-1912
Marine Investment Co	Greenock	1865-1867
Marshall and Co	Maryhill, Glasgow	1890-1910
James Munn	Greenock	1760-1820
P Murchie	Port Glasgow	1837-1852
Murdoch and Murray	Port Glasgow	1875-1912
Henry Murray and Co	Port Glasgow	1867-1882
Henry Murray and Co	Dumbarton	1881-1884
Murray Brothers	Dumbarton	1883-1891
Murries and Clark	Greenock	1831-1844
Napier and Miller Ltd	Yoker/Old Kilpatrick	1898-1906
Napier, Shanks and Bell	Yoker	1877-1898
David Napier	Lancefield, Glasgow	1821-1836

James Napier and Hoey	Govan	1850-1858
Robert Napier and Sons	Lancefield/Govan	1836-1900
Thomas Orr, Junior	Greenock	1883-1899
Randolph, Elder and Co	Govan/Fairfield	1860-1870
John Reid and Co	Port Glasgow/Whiteinch	1847-1909
Reid and Hanna	Paisley	1816-1851
Reid and Hanna	Greenock	1833-1836
Ritchie, Graham and Milne	Govan/Whiteinch	1891-1922
Alexander Robertson and Sons	Sandbank	1876-
Robertson and Co	Greenock	1865-1869
A Rodger and Co	Port Glasgow	1891-1912
Ross and Marshall Limited	Greenock	1899-1925
Russell	Greenock	1867-1868
Russell and Co	Greenock/Port Glasgow	1874-1918
Scott and Sons(Bowling) Ltd	Bowling	1851-1979
Scott and McGill	Bowling	1850's
J E Scott	Greenock	1874-1879
Scott and Linton	Dumbarton	1867-1870
Scott's Shipbuilding and Engineering Company Limited	Greenock	1711-
T B Seath and Co	Partick/Rutherglen	1853-1902
John Shearer and Son	Kelvinhaugh/Elderslie	1890-1912
William Simons and Co	Greenock/Whiteinch/ Renfrew	1810-1957
Smith and Rodger	Govan	1843-1864
Robert Steele and Co	Greenock	1816-1883
Steele and Carswell	Greenock	1796-1816
Alexander Stephen and Sons	Kelvinhaugh/Linthouse	1851-1968
J & R Swan	Dumbarton	1870-1874
Swan	Port Dundas/Maryhill Kelvindock	1857-1888
R Taylerson	Port Glasgow	1858-1859
Taylor and Mitchell	Greenock	1898-1900
W B Thomson and Co	Whiteinch	1880-1886
J & G Thomson	Govan/Clydebank	1851-1897
Thomson and Spiers	Greenock	1840-1842
Tod and MacGregor	Mavisbank/Meadowside	1834-1873
Troon Shipbuilding Co	Troon	1860's-1885
Thomas Wingate and Co	Springfield/Whiteinch	1837-1878
Charles Wood	Dumbarton	1835-1843
John Wood and Co	Greenock/Port Glasgow	1780-1853

Bibliography

The Second City	Oakley	Blackie 1976
Clyde Shipbuilding from Old Photographs	Hume/Moss	Batsford 1975
Clyde Navigation	J Riddell	Donald 1979
Burrell - Portrait of a Collector	R Marks	Richard Drew 1983
Workshop of the British Empire: Engineering and Shipbuilding in the West of Scotland	Hume/Moss	Heinemann 1977
Song of the Clyde	Walker	PSL 1984
History of Clydebank	J Hood (ed)	Parthenon 1988
Old Docks	Ritchie-Noakes	Shire 1987
Half of Glasgow's Gone	M Dick	Brown, Son & Ferguson 1987
The Guinness Book of Ships and Shipping	Hartman (ed)	Guiness 1983
Historic Cunard Liners	Rentell	Atlantic Transport 1986
Merchants Fleets (in profile): Nos 1: P & O, Orient and Blue Anchor No 9: Anchor Line No 11: British India No 12: Cunard Line No 13: Donaldson Line No 10: Shaw, Savill and Albion No 15: T & J Harrison	D Haws	TCL (Various)
Flagships of the Line	M Watson	PSL 1988
The Story of the P & O	Howarth/Howarth	Weidenfield & Nicholson 1986
The Pirrie Kylsant Motorships	Mallet & Bell	Mallet & Bell 1984
The British Seafarer	Mason, Greenhill, and Craig	Hutchison/BBC 1980
Fifty Famous Liners (3 Vols)	Braynard/Miller	PSL 1982/85/87
Majesty at Sea	Shaum & Flayhart	PSL 1981
Victorian and Edwardian Steamships from old Photographs	Greenhill/Gifford	Batsford 1979
Passenger Ships of the Orient Line	McCart	PSL 1987
20th Century Passenger Ships of the P & O	McCart	PSL 1985
North Atlantic Seaway (5 Vols)	Bonsor	Brookside 1976
Great passenger Ships of the World (6 Vols)	Kludas	PSL 1975/76/77/87
North Atlantic Run	Maxtone Graham	Cassel 1972
Clyde and other Coastal Steamers	Duckworth/Langmuir	Stephenson 1977
Clyde River and other Steamers	Duckworth/Langmuir	Brown, Son & Ferguson 1972
West Highland Steamers	Duckworth/Langmuir	Stephenson 1967
John Brown's Body	J McLauchlan,	Strathclyde Region 1975
The Structure of British Industry Volume 2,	Cairncross,	Parkinson 1958

Bibliography continued

Growth and Decline of
Clyde Shipbuilding   M S Moss,   Education for Industrial
                                                   Society Project 1986

The Fairfield Report   J D Houston   University of Strathclyde
Regional Studies Group, Bulletin No 8   1967
British Shipbuilding 1972   HMSO from Lloyds Register
                                                   of Shipping 1972

Sea Breezes Magazine   Various editions